Shakespeare-ience
Romeo and Juliet

Dr. Robert D. Strickland

Perfection Learning® Corporation
Logan, Iowa 51546-0500

Editorial Director	Julie A. Schumacher
Editorial Research and Feature Writer	Wim Coleman
Design	Kay Ewald
Art Research	Lisa Lorimor
Cover Art	Michael Aspengren

Copyright © 2002 **Perfection Learning Corporation**
1000 North Second Avenue, P.O. Box 500
Logan, Iowa 51546-0500
Tel: 1-800-831-4190 • Fax: 1-800-543-2745

Printed in the United States of America

Paperback ISBN 0-7891-5686-5
Cover Craft ISBN 0-7569-0737-3

Table of Contents

Introductory Material

The Play

Dr. Robert D. Strickland is Executive Director in the Division of Life Skills and Special Projects for all of the arts disciplines in the Miami-Dade County Public Schools. He received a BS in Music Education from the University of Tennessee, a MA and MFA in Theatre from the University of Miami, and an Ed.D in Educational Leadership from Nova Southeastern University. He is a past President of the Florida Association for Theatre Education and a member of the Florida Department of Education writing team for the theatre teacher certification examination, theatre curriculum frameworks/standards, and theatre course descriptions. He was a Senior Consultant for developing and writing a high school textbook that received the 1999 Distinguished Book Award from the American Alliance for Theatre Education.

Dr. Strickland has taught at the elementary, secondary, college, and university levels. He received the 1997 Administrator of the Year awards from both the Florida Association for Theatre Education and the Dade Association for Theatre Education. In 2000, Dr. Strickland was awarded the Herbert A. Drew, Jr., Memorial Award for Excellence in Education from Nova Southeastern University.

Dr. Strickland participated in the conceptualization of *Shakespeare-ience*, as well as the writing and editing of the program.

Wim Coleman, a freelance novelist and playwright, has frequently written about Shakespeare for students. Mr. Coleman holds a MA in Teaching in both English and education from Drake University. A seasoned theatre professional, Coleman has worked as an actor, director, set designer, and scene shop manager. He has taught, directed, and performed in *Romeo and Juliet* and has edited several Shakespeare plays in Perfection Learning's popular Parallel Text series.

Mr. Coleman wrote several background essays for *Romeo and Juliet* as well as the informational notes found at the bottom of most pages.

About This Program

This program was designed to help you discover the world of Shakespeare and in particular the story of Romeo and Juliet. Shakespeare's plays were meant to be seen and heard. In his day, rowdy audiences responded to them with applause, tears, and jeers. The plays were printed mainly for the use of actors, so naturally students did not study them as they do today.

This book takes the fear out of studying Shakespeare and puts back the fun. Our approach to *Romeo and Juliet* is different in several important ways.

- Every student will be creating a character or persona that will live within the context of the play. You will participate every day, not just the days you are reading the part of one of the characters with lines in the text.

- You will find that Shakespeare is not that difficult, contrary to what you might have heard. We have provided you with a number of guiding features, such as on-page plot summaries, word and phrase definitions, and historical insights, to help you with the places that might be troublesome.

- By examining the thoughts of the characters through improvisation and then applying your understanding of the character's actions to the script, you will speak and hear the words of Shakespeare as he intended. You'll find that the words on these pages come to life when the art of theatre is used to study them.

Have fun with this program. While you probably won't mount a full production of *Romeo and Juliet*, you will learn to hurl insults Shakespearean-style (you vile, lean-witted cur!). You will learn to use hand and body gestures, expressive speech, and blocking (simple movements) as you read. If you trust yourself and jump into examining this world through the eyes of Shakespeare's characters and your own personas, you will truly have a Shakespeare-ience.

The Story of *Romeo and Juliet*

Boy meets girl. They fall in love. Their families are bitter enemies. The result? Tragedy.

This is the bare outline of *Romeo and Juliet*. To fill it in, imagine a sunny summer morning in the town of Verona, Italy, during the Renaissance. Here, two servants from the Capulet household are strolling through the public square. The pair soon picks a fight with rival servants from the Montague household. (The Capulets and Montagues have bitterly quarreled for so many years that nobody even knows how their feud began.)

When a fight begins, a young man from the house of Montague, named Benvolio, tries to make peace. A fiery Capulet called Tybalt resists this effort and escalates the quarrel. Onlookers soon take sides. They are joined by the elderly lords of the two warring households, whose exasperated wives restrain them from joining in.

Prince Escalus, the ruler of Verona, comes upon the scene and demands that the fighting stop. In the quarrel's aftermath, Lord Montague asks Benvolio why his son, Romeo, seems so depressed. Romeo has been avoiding his friends, but a determined Benvolio tracks him down. He learns that Romeo is in love with Rosaline, a girl who has no interest in him. Benvolio vows to make Romeo forget her.

Meanwhile in the Capulet household, Lord Capulet and a nobleman named Paris discuss Paris's proposal of marriage to Lord Capulet's thirteen-year-old daughter, Juliet. Their discussion turns to the masked banquet the Capulets are hosting that night, and ends with both hoping that Juliet will get to know Paris and agree to marry him. Of course, the hated Montagues are not invited to the banquet. When Benvolio and Romeo catch wind of it, though, they decide to go in disguise. During the party, Tybalt guesses their identity and vows revenge on Romeo whom, he assumes, has come only to mock the Capulets and cause trouble.

Meanwhile, Juliet catches Romeo's eye, and he instantly forgets Rosaline. By the time Romeo and Juliet realize they are from warring families, it is too late: they have already fallen in love. With the help of the Nurse, the servant who has taken care of Juliet since infancy, the two are secretly married the next day. Friar Lawrence, a churchman and friend of Romeo who hopes the marriage will end the feud between the families, conducts the ceremony.

As Romeo is walking home from the secret wedding, he comes upon Benvolio and their mutual friend, Mercutio, who is quarreling with Tybalt. Romeo tries but fails to break up the fight between them. Tybalt fatally stabs Mercutio, and, in turn, Romeo avenges his friend's death by killing Tybalt. A furious Prince Escalus bans Romeo from Verona, warning that he will be put to death if he ever returns.

Romeo and Juliet are in despair over Romeo's banishment, but their allies, the Nurse and Friar Lawrence, come to the rescue once more. They arrange for the couple to spend the night together before Romeo leaves for exile in Mantua. Lord Capulet, however, not knowing that Juliet is already married, has arranged for her to marry Paris. He bellows with outrage when she refuses.

Juliet brings her problem to Friar Lawrence, who devises a daring plan. He directs Juliet to pretend to change her mind and agree to marry Paris. The night before the wedding, however, she must drink a potion that will put her in a death-like state for forty-two hours. The Friar reasons that her body will be taken to the Capulet burial vault. Romeo, who has already left for Mantua, will receive a letter from Friar Lawrence letting him know of the plan and instructing him to arrive at the vault just as

Juliet wakes. The two can then leave for Mantua where they will begin their married life.

Unfortunately, the plan goes terribly wrong when Romeo hears that Juliet is dead but does not receive Friar Lawrence's letter telling him that the death is false. A distraught Romeo buys poison with which to kill himself and then rushes back to Verona to die alongside the body of his young wife. When he arrives at the vault, however, he learns that he is not alone. Paris, who had planned to marry Juliet, is there placing flowers at her tomb. Romeo fatally wounds Paris, but honors his rival's dying request to be placed in the vault next to Juliet. Romeo then drinks poison and dies just as Juliet is awakening from her deep sleep. When she realizes in horror what has happened, Juliet takes Romeo's dagger and stabs herself.

Word of the deaths quickly spreads through the town along with news of another tragic event—Romeo's mother has died of grief over her son's banishment. The play ends when the heads of the warring households, Lords Montague and Capulet, agree to end their feud and erect a golden monument to their children.

Working with Shakespeare's Language

When you first begin reading Shakespeare, you may find his language intimidating and confusing. You will discover, however, that the more Shakespeare you read and the more you know about his writing, the easier it becomes.

Keep in mind that language is a living thing, constantly growing and changing. New words are invented and new definitions for old words are added. Since Shakespeare wrote over 400 years ago, it is not surprising that his work seems challenging to today's readers. To help you with the meaning of the text, unfamiliar words and phrases have been defined for you in the side margins of this book. You may also find a dictionary helpful for this purpose. Beyond the meaning of the words, however, there are stylistic devices that can help you understand Shakespeare.

Blank Verse and Iambic Pentameter

Like most dramatists of his time, Shakespeare wrote his plays in **blank verse**. Blank verse simply means that the text is written in measured lines that look like poetry, but do not rhyme. Look at the following example.

> He jests at scars that never felt a wound.
> But soft what light through yonder window breaks?
> It is the east, and Juliet is the sun.
> Arise, fair sun, and kill the envious moon,

You can see that the four lines above are approximately equal in length, but they do not cover the whole width of the page as the lines in a story or essay might. They are, in fact, unrhymed verse with each line containing ten or eleven syllables. Furthermore, the ten syllables can be divided into five sections, called **iambs**. Each iamb contains one stressed (\) and one unstressed (U) syllable. Try reading the lines below, giving emphasis to the capitalized syllable in each iamb.

U \	U \	U \	U \	U \
He JESTS	at SCARS	that NEV	er FELT	a WOUND.

U \	U \	U \	U \	U \
But SOFT!	what LIGHT	through YON	der WIN	dow BREAKS?

The length of a line of verse is measured by counting the stresses. This length is known as the **meter** and when there are five stresses, as in the preceding lines, the pattern is known as **iambic pentameter**.

Of course, Shakespeare was not rigid about this format. He sometimes varied the lines by putting accents in unusual places, by having lines with more or fewer than ten syllables, and by varying where pauses occur. An actor's interpretation can also add variety. (Only a terrible actor would deliver lines in a way that makes the rhythm sound obvious or repetitious!)

Prose

In addition to verse, Shakespeare wrote speeches in **prose**, which is language without rhythmic structure. Look at the examples on page 37. Try beating out the rhythm of Capulet's speech which is at the top of the page, and you will find that it follows the pattern of iambic pentameter. But if you try to impose the same rhythm on the servant's speech that follows, you'll discover that it doesn't work at all. Shakespeare generally used prose for comic speeches, to show madness, and for characters of lower social rank such as servants. Verse was reserved for the upper classes. Like all other rules, however, Shakespeare felt free to break these patterns whenever he liked.

Imagery

Imagery refers to vibrant, colorful language that allows readers or listeners to picture things in their mind's eye and to make an emotional connection with the writing. This highly descriptive language appeals to one or more of the five senses— touch, taste, hearing, smell, and sight. How many sensory images can you find in the following speech?

> O, bid me leap, rather than marry Paris,
> From off the battlements of yonder
>   tower;
> Or walk in thievish ways; or bid me lurk
> Where serpents are; chain me with
>   roaring bears;
> Or shut me nightly in a charnel-house,
> O'er-cover'd quite with dead men's
>   rattling bones,
> With reeky shanks and yellow chapless
>   skulls;

In addition to sensory words, images are often conveyed through the use of **figures of speech** such as simile, metaphor, or personification.

A **simile** is a comparison between two unlike things that uses the words *like* or *as.* Look at the following examples.

> she hangs upon the cheek of night like a
>   rich jewel in an Ethiop's ear

> Love goes toward love as schoolboys
>   from their books

In the first example, Romeo says that Juliet is like a rich jewel; in the second, he compares the eagerness of lovers meeting each other with the eagerness of boys leaving their schoolwork behind.

A **metaphor** is also a comparison between two unlike things, but the words *like* or *as* are left out.

> My lips, two blushing pilgrims, ready stand
>
> Juliet is the Sun
>
> Yond light . . . it is some meteor that the sun exhales

Another type of imagery used extensively by Shakespeare is **personification**, or giving human qualities to inanimate objects or ideas. In the following lines, desire is personified as an old man lying down to die and night is described as wearing a cloak.

> Now old desire doth in his deathbed lie
>
> I have night's cloak to hide me from their sight

Contractions

As you know, contractions are words that have been combined by substituting an apostrophe for a letter or letters that have been removed. Contractions were as common in Shakespeare's time as they are today. For example, we use *it's* as a contraction for the words *it is*. In Shakespeare's writing you will discover that *'tis* means the same thing. Many other examples can be found on the list of Frequently Used Words on pages 212–213.

Shakespeare often used the apostrophe to shorten words so that they would fit into the rhythm pattern of a line. This is especially true of verbs ending in *-ed*. Note that in Shakespeare's plays, the *-ed* at the end of a verb is pronounced as a separate syllable. Therefore, *walked* would be pronounced as two syllables, *walk•ed*, while *walk'd* would be only one.

You will learn about other elements of Shakespeare's language such as **puns**, **malapropisms**, **oxymorons**, and **irony** as they occur in the text.

Finally, if you can't figure out every word in the play, don't get discouraged. The people in Shakespeare's audience couldn't either. At that time, language was changing rapidly and standardized spelling, punctuation, and grammar and even dictionaries did not exist. Besides, Shakespeare loved to play with words. He made up new combinations, like *fat-guts* and *mumble-news*. He often changed one part of speech for another, as in "cursing claims and deep *exclaims*." To make matters worse, the actors probably spoke at a rate of 140 words per minute. But the audience didn't strain to catch every word. They went to a Shakespeare play for the same reasons we go to a movie—to get caught up in the story and the acting, to have a great laugh, an exciting adventure, or a good cry.

Strategies for Reading Shakespeare

You will find many features in this book designed to help you understand Shakespeare's language. In addition, there are some basic reading strategies that active readers use for all types of text. As you prepare to read *Romeo and Juliet,* you may find the following strategic plan useful.

Preview. First, to get a general idea of the events in the play, "read the edges" of the text. Read the summaries at the top of each page. Then skim the definitions and questions in the side margins and examine any images that appear. This will give you a general idea of what the text is about before you actually begin to read it.

Visualize. Try to put yourself "into" the Renaissance by picturing the setting in your mind's eye. Try to envision how the characters might look and sound as they move within their surroundings. Studying images and reading through the setting and stage directions will help to fire up your imagination.

Read. Read a page using the side notes to help with difficult words and phrases. Go back and reread the page a second time or as many times as necessary until you can understand the text without using the side notes. You should expect that this will be more difficult in the beginning and take

more time than reading modern writing, but don't be discouraged. Most students find that comprehension becomes easier and easier as the play goes on.

Connect. Active readers often make connections with the text. An event in their reading might remind them of something that happened to them or a friend, or they might see similarities between the text and a movie, book, or TV show they have seen. Also, because Shakespeare is quoted so frequently, readers are likely to come across familiar phrases and sayings.

Evaluate. As you read, evaluate the characters' words and actions and form opinions about them. Do you agree or disagree with how they act? What are their motives? What are their strengths and weaknesses? Do certain actions make you change your mind about a character?

Enrich. Surround your study of *Romeo and Juliet* with humor and high-interest material. The notes at the bottom of most pages and the essays at the back of the book provide background information. The "Tales from the Stage" feature contains colorful theatrical anecdotes. The suggestions for props and in-class staging also help to immerse you in Shakespeare's world.

Preparing for Speaking Parts

At least once during your study of *Romeo and Juliet*, you will be assigned a speaking part to perform for an upcoming class. In order to feel comfortable in this role and to respect the efforts of other students reading with you, you will need to prepare beforehand. If you are unsure about how to do this, try using the following plan.

Comprehend. Make sure you understand the meaning of what your character says. If you are unsure, use the reading strategies on page 12.

Analyze. Determine your character's attitude during the scene. What mood is he in? Does this mood change during the scene? Are her thoughts and what she says the same? Or does she say one thing and mean another? What is your character's motivation? What does he want? What is his attitude toward other characters in the scene? Is there a conflict? What is it?

Plan. Decide how you will use your body and voice to create your character. What gestures will you use? Where and when will you move? How will you use your voice? Changes in the tempo (fast, slow); pitch (high, low); and quality (nasal, raspy, etc.) of your voice can help the audience understand your character. If needed, you can put sticky notes in your text to remind you of where you want to change your voice or move.

Practice. You probably won't have a chance to rehearse with others in your scene, but you should still practice your own part. Ask a friend or family member to read lines with you and/or videotape you. You can also practice reading your part in front of a mirror and/or into a tape recorder.

Warm Up. Here are a few exercises to make your voice and body more flexible and responsive.

- Stand tall and inhale on a count of four; hold your breath for a count of four; and then exhale on a count of eight. Make sure that your shoulders are relaxed and do not rise up as you breathe. Your lower stomach area should be slowly moving out as you inhale, and in as you exhale.

- Next, repeat the same exercise and while you are exhaling, hum the letter M. You will feel a tingle in your face from the vibration of the sound. After you have done this several times, try a few tongue twisters. Here is one to start with:

  Amidst the mists and coldest frosts,
  With stoutest wrists and loudest boasts,
  He thrusts his fists against the post
  And still insists he sees the ghosts.

- Stand tall with your feet shoulder-width apart. Bend over slowly and reach for or touch the floor. Relax and breathe. Bend your knees more and then straighten your legs slowly. Slowly round up your body to a standing position. Repeat the whole exercise twice.

Act and React. As you present your scene, remember to face the "audience" and speak loudly enough to be heard throughout the room. If you hold your book up, your voice will project out and not down into the book. Finally, listen, really listen, to what the other characters are saying so that you can respond realistically and pick up cues promptly.

How to Have a Shakespeare-ience

There is an old saying that to really understand someone you need to walk a mile in his or her shoes. This study of *Romeo and Juliet* borrows from that old adage by asking you to study this play by becoming a character from 14th-century Verona. You will "walk" for many days in that person's "shoes."

By seeing the world of Verona through eyes other than your own, you will gain a new perspective and interact with other characters that shape that world. Not all of the characters that you create actually speak within the text of the play, but all are affected by the circumstances and actions of the speaking characters. So you may not be Romeo, but you may be his attendant or Valentine, Mercutio's brother. You may not be Juliet, but you may be Rosaline or Juliet's maid.

All of you will be part of the action of the play, and from time to time will be called upon to be one of the traditional speaking characters as well. In addition, you will be creating events and situations that are only implied by the action of the play. For example, there is a masquerade banquet and dance that takes place at the Capulet house. If you were a servant to the Capulets, what would your duties be in preparing for the festivities? And if you were to create a scene that happens just before or just after the banquet with the other servants, what do you think would be the focus of that scene? And,

as the story of the play unfolds, how do the various events that take place affect you and your world?

You will be discovering what life was like in the world of Verona hundreds of years ago. The creation of your character, or **persona**, as we will call it throughout the rest of this book, will be based on elements in the text, historical information, human nature, and your imagination. You will discover the events that influenced the lives of the people of this Italian town and ultimately played important roles in the unfolding of this story. By being immersed this way in the story and the play, you will experience *Romeo and Juliet* as if you were there. This is what we mean by having a **Shakespeare–ience**.

Choosing Your Persona

There are dozens of people that make up the population of Verona, as seen in the following lists. Your instructor may assign one of these characters to you or may ask you to choose your own. In either case, you will begin with only a name or occupation. It will be your job to develop this persona and turn him or her into a complete character. You will begin by answering questions and developing a personality profile for your persona. The easiest way to keep track of your character is to use a journal. As the play progresses, you will find questions and directions, labeled **Persona Journal** and **Persona Action,** which will guide you.

Nonspeaking Characters Mentioned in the Play

Signor Martino
County Anselme
Signor Placentio
Valentine, brother of Mercutio
Signor Valentio, cousin of Tybalt

Lucio
Rosaline, cousin to Juliet
Signora Martino, wife of Signor Martino
Daughters of Signor Martino

Sisters of County Anselme
Widow Vitruvio
Nieces of Signor Placentio
Wife of Capulet's Uncle

Daughters of Capulet's Uncle
Livia
Helena

Citizens of Verona

The following people make up Verona's population. They include all kinds of occupations, all ages, and all levels of society. They may be neutral or they may sympathize with either the Capulets or the Montagues.

Cook
Masker
Watchman
Attendant
Page
Squire
Jester
Secretary
Copyist
Astrologist
Maid
Dueling master
Physician
Seamstress
Embroiderer
Launderer
Crier
Weaver
Emissary
Musician
Minstrel

Apothecary
Ink maker
Wine maker
Church official
Small landowner
Guard stable keeper
Potter
Farmer
Mule driver
Street cleaner
Tailor
Furrier
Shoemaker
Tannery worker
Mill worker
Beer maker
Olive oil maker
Roofer
Stone mason
Iron/lead worker
Wood carver

Painter
Barber
Candle maker
Serf/peasant
Scribe
Baker
Soldier
Carpenter
Steward (oversaw lord's estate)
Craftsman
Blacksmith
Beekeeper
Shepherd
Hunter
Tax collector
Rent collector
Toll collector on rivers, bridges, or roads
Notary
Banker

Money maker (coinage)
Goldsmith
Scribes
Soap maker
Fishmonger
Hatters
Cabinet maker
Lawyer
Merchant
Dye worker
Inn keeper
Butler
Master of Falconry and the Hunt
Jester
Count/Countess
Duke/Duchess

Understanding Improvisation

It is possible that you have heard the word improvisation in connection to theatre, music, stand-up comedy, or dance. Improvisation may sometimes be referred to as role-playing. In this study of *Romeo and Juliet*, improvisation exercises before each scene will be used as a discovery tool to explore the characters and the events in the play.

Literally, to improvise is to speak or act out a situation without a script or preconceived way of presenting the scene. You are given the framework of the situation such as the conflict and the characters, and without advanced planning, you make up the scene dialogue spontaneously. In the situations you examine, you must find a way to resolve the conflicts and overcome the obstacles in order to accomplish the objectives of the characters. Your concentration should be directed toward the situation and the other participants, while you keep an open mind about what your character is experiencing. In addition, be receptive to any new information introduced by your partner(s). An honest reaction on your part is what is expected.

Improvisation trains people to think on different levels. It helps develop imagination, concentration, self-esteem, self-confidence, observation skills, listening skills, problem-solving skills, and thinking skills.

The following exercises will introduce you to the process of improvisation.

Partner Activities

- You meet someone and fall in love instantly. Now tell them.
- You tell a trusted friend that against your parent's wishes, you are going to marry someone they hate.
- Tease a friend about someone they have fallen in love with.
- Respond to someone who has insulted your best friend.
- Warn your best friend about someone they are interested in dating.

Group Activities

With a group of seven to ten students, improvise waiting in an express checkout line (only ten items) at a grocery store. One customer has more than ten items, and their friend keeps bringing more items as you wait. The checkout person is working their first day after completing training.

With a group of ten to fifteen students, improvise a situation where a local radio station is doing a remote location set-up, and as a promotion is giving away tickets to an upcoming concert. There are only three pairs of tickets to give away, and more than ten people show up to win them. Each person must convince the DJ to give him or her the tickets.

Romeo and Juliet Warm-ups

- Capulet and Lady Capulet are making a list of guests for the feast, and planning all of the other details for the party.
- Romeo is convincing his parents that he should be allowed to go out that evening (without telling them he is going to the Capulet party).
- Romeo tries to explain to his parents where he has been all night.
- Romeo begins to speak to his parents about the Capulet feud, intending to test the waters about dating Juliet.
- Rosaline sees Romeo talking to Juliet and now decides that she wants Romeo for herself. She plans what to do to win him back while discussing her thoughts with a friend.
- Romeo tries to talk to Benvolio about his love for Juliet.

Insults—Shakespearean Style

The rich language of Shakespeare's day lent itself to especially colorful insults. As a persona in a city where fighting often breaks out, it's always useful to have a good insult or two available when needed. To create an insult, choose a word from each column below. Begin with "Thou," and then add your A, B, C word choices in order. For example: "Thou crusty, toad-spotted dunghill!" Practice speaking your insult until it sounds appropriately derogatory.

A	B	C
foul	motley-minded	bloodsucker
impudent	beetle-headed	knave
peevish	glass-faced	dastard
swaggering	hag-seeded	rabble
testy	wide-chapped	carrion
contagious	bunch-backed	gaud
viperous	shrill-voiced	jack-dog
banished	lean-witted	lubber
injurious	dull-eyed	want-wit
tedious	base-born	flibbertigibbet
vile	brazen-faced	dunghill
noisome	milk-livered	wanton
deceitful	dog-hearted	clod
filthy	toad-spotted	wretch
beastly	sheep-whistling	cur
loathsome	pigeon-livered	rogue
clamorous	lily-livered	ingrate
unvirtuous	whey-faced	ragamuffin
wrangling	long-tongued	dotard
insinuating	white-livered	milksop
murderous	shame-faced	maltworm
venomed	mouse-eaten	sot
rancourous	wall-eyed	churl
usurping	sheep-biting	strumpet
mangy	idle-headed	rogue
crusty	lack-brained	dolt
ruinous	rump-fed	maggot-pie
putrefied	loggerheaded	drudge
babbling	smooth-faced	haggard
leprous	clay-brained	stench
villainous	fat-kidneyed	wretch
cankered	shallow-hearted	sluggard

Welcome to Renaissance Verona!

It is July, and you are a citizen of Verona, a city in northern Italy. You have awakened on this wonderful summer morning and begun your day. You make your way to the town square for a reason in keeping with the occupation and/or social status of your persona: to shop, to sell, to meet a friend, to hear the latest gossip, to go for a walk, and so forth. You enter the square and mime your chosen task. Keep in mind that Verona has not been peaceful for quite a while, due to a long-standing feud between two important Veronese families—the Capulets and the Montagues. This feud has forced many people to take sides and has made the whole town tense.

As you go about your morning's business and quietly improvise conversations with other townsfolk, someone instigates a mild verbal confrontation with another citizen. You look around to see what is taking place, and "in persona," you enter into the disagreement by hurling insults at others. Gradually, three distinct groups begin to form—those who side with the Capulets (who gather on the side of the classroom closest to the door), those who favor the Montagues (who are on the opposite side of the room), and a third group that is, for the time being, neutral (grouped at the back of the classroom). Safe within the protection of your group, you continue to hurl insults at the other two groups.

When the activity ends, answer the following questions in your Persona Journal.

- What were you doing before the confrontation began?
- How did it start?
- Which group did you join?
- How did you react to the insults directed towards you?
- Were you surprised by the reactions of others in your group? in the other groups?

Woodcut print of medieval town of Verona, 1493

Romeo and Juliet

ACT I

Leonard Whiting and Olivia Hussey in Franco Zeffirelli's 1968 film of *Romeo and Juliet*.

"A pair of star-cross'd lovers . . ."

Cast of Characters

THE HOUSE OF CAPULET

JULIET
LORD CAPULET her father
LADY CAPULET her mother
NURSE servant to Juliet
PETER servant to the Nurse
TYBALT first cousin to Juliet and nephew to Lady Capulet
2 CAPULET Capulet's kinsman
SAMPSON servant to Capulet
GREGORY servant to Capulet
POTPAN servant to Capulet
other SERVANTS

THE HOUSE OF MONTAGUE

ROMEO
LORD MONTAGUE his father
LADY MONTAGUE his mother
BENVOLIO first cousin to Romeo and nephew to Lord Montague
BALTHASAR servant to Romeo
ABRAHAM servant to Montague

OTHERS

CHORUS actor who introduces Acts I and II
ESCALUS prince of Verona
PARIS young nobleman and kinsman to the Prince
PAGE servant to Paris
MERCUTIO friend to Romeo and kinsman to the Prince
FRIAR LAWRENCE Franciscan priest
FRIAR JOHN Franciscan priest
APOTHECARY pharmacist from Mantua
MUSICIANS, CITIZENS, TORCH-BEARERS, GUARDS,
    SERVANTS, ATTENDANTS, WATCHMEN, KINSMEN from both houses

TIME the fourteenth century

PLACE Verona and Mantua, cities in northern Italy

One actor referred to as the CHORUS appears on stage and speaks directly to the audience. He previews the events of the play, explaining that it involves two feuding families and the tragedy that occurs when their children meet and fall in love.

THE PROLOGUE

[Enter CHORUS.]

CHORUS. Two households, both alike in dignity,
    In fair Verona, where we lay our scene,
From ancient grudge break to new mutiny,
    Where civil blood makes civil hands unclean.
From forth the fatal loins of these two foes   5
    A pair of star-cross'd lovers take their life;
Whose misadventur'd piteous overthrows
    Doth with their death bury their parents' strife.
The fearful passage of their death-mark'd love,
    And the continuance of their parents' rage,   10
Which but their children's end naught could remove,
*   Is now the two hours' traffic of our stage;
The which, if you with patient ears attend,
What here shall miss, our toil shall strive to mend.

❓ Skim this speech and decide how you think it should be spoken. Is the Chorus serious or lighthearted, loud or soft, still or moving?

3 mutiny: fighting

4 civil blood: blood of Verona's citizens

6 star-cross'd: doomed; **take their life:** are born

7 misadventur'd piteous overthrows: tragic events

12 traffic: action

14 What . . . mend: We'll try to fill in any details that I've left out of this introduction.

* **". . . two hours' traffic . . ."** Could Shakespeare's actors really have performed *Romeo and Juliet* in only two hours? Although he says so in his prologue, today's actors find it difficult to play it in less than three, so it is nearly always cut for stage or screen. To perform *Romeo and Juliet* in two hours, the actors would have to speak at a rate of about 200 words per minute. To see for yourself how hard this is, try reading aloud the above prologue (a sonnet) in thirty seconds.

Setting the Scene

ROMEO AND JULIET
Act I, scene i *or* Boys Will Be Boys

Critical Query: What's troubling the men of Verona?

From the Prop Box

Ribbons of three different colors. The Capulet household wears one color; Montagues another. All others wear the third color.

Insults and Vulgar Vocab

poor-John	dried fish, a cheap food thought to reduce the sex drive
maidenhead	virginity
thrust, push, feel, stand, pretty piece of flesh, tool, naked weapon	words used because of their sexual meaning

Time Capsule

In Shakespeare's day, people took astrology and horoscopes very seriously. Romeo and Juliet are referred to as "star-cross'd" lovers because the position of the stars was unfavorable when they were born.

Classroom Set Design

Move desks back to allow space for an acting area. Those from the house of Capulet sit on one side of the room; Montagues sit on the other. Family crests or banners may be drawn and put on the walls to identify sides. Royalty and neutral citizens may sit on either side.

```
                                    ┌──────┐
                                    │ Desk │
            Acting Area             └──────┘

          ☐ ☐ ☐          ☐ ☐ ☐

          ☐ ☐ ☐          ☐ ☐ ☐

       Capulets            Montagues
```

Warm-up Improv 1

Several young men are hanging out, making silly jokes, and bragging about how macho they are. A rival gang appears and makes threats. Friends from both groups appear and a brawl begins. The police arrive to break things up and everyone scatters.

Warm-up Improv 2

(Use after page 30.) You are at your school locker with one or two friends. You are head-over-heels in love, but the object of your affection is ignoring you. Your friends try to cheer you up. The bell rings and everyone heads for class.

The scene opens on a public square in Verona, Italy. Two Capulet servants, Sampson and Gregory, enter carrying swords and small shields [bucklers]. They begin to trade silly puns and boast about their adventures with women.

Scene i. A Public Place

[Enter SAMPSON *and* GREGORY *armed with swords and bucklers.]*

✱ **SAMPSON.** Gregory, o' my word, we'll not carry coals.

GREGORY. No, for then we should be colliers.

SAMPSON. I mean, an we be in choler we'll draw.

GREGORY. Ay, while you live, draw your neck out o' the collar.

SAMPSON. I strike quickly, being moved.   5

GREGORY. But thou art not quickly moved to strike.

SAMPSON. A dog of the house of Montague moves me.

GREGORY. To move is to stir; and to be valiant is to stand: therefore, if thou art moved, thou runn'st away.

SAMPSON. A dog of that house shall move me to stand: I will take   10 the wall of any man or maid of Montague's.

GREGORY. That shows thee a weak slave; for the weakest goes to the wall.

SAMPSON. True; and therefore women, being the weaker vessels, are ever thrust to the wall: therefore I will push Montague's   15 men from the wall and thrust his maids to the wall.

GREGORY. The quarrel is between our masters and us their men.

SAMPSON. 'Tis all one, I will show myself a tyrant: when I have fought with the men I will be cruel with the maids, I will cut off their heads.   20

✱ **Playing to the Crowd**   Is a string of coarse jokes and a street brawl any way to start a love story? Shakespeare may have done it this way to capture the attention of his informal open-air theatre audience. Playgoers called "groundlings" paid little admission and had to stand up through the entire show. Uneducated and easily bored, they were given to heckling the actors. How better to entertain them than with crude humor and violence?

As Sampson and Gregory continue to brag, two Montague servants appear, and Sampson urges Gregory to pick a fight. The servants from both houses begin to insult each other.

GREGORY. The heads of the maids?

SAMPSON. Ay, the heads of the maids, or their maidenheads; take it in what sense thou wilt.

GREGORY. They must take it in sense that feel it.

SAMPSON. Me they shall feel while I am able to stand: and 'tis 25 known I am a pretty piece of flesh.

GREGORY. 'Tis well thou art not fish; if thou hadst, thou hadst been poor-John.—Draw thy tool; Here comes two of the house of Montagues.

[Enter ABRAHAM and BALTHASAR.]

SAMPSON. My naked weapon is out: quarrel! I will back thee. 30

GREGORY. How! turn thy back and run?

SAMPSON. Fear me not.

GREGORY. No, marry; I fear thee!

SAMPSON. Let us take the law of our sides; let them begin.

GREGORY. I will frown as I pass by; and let them take it as they list. 35

✱ **SAMPSON.** Nay, as they dare. I will bite my thumb at them; which is disgrace to them if they bear it.

ABRAHAM. Do you bite your thumb at us, sir?

SAMPSON. I do bite my thumb, sir.

ABRAHAM. Do you bite your thumb at us, sir? 40

SAMPSON. *[Aside to GREGORY.]* Is the law of our side if I say ay?

GREGORY. *[Aside to SAMPSON.]* No.

22 or their maidenheads: a bawdy pun meaning he will rob the women of their virginity

❓ How would you read the lines that have sexual references so that the audience will not miss your meaning?

28 poor-John: salted fish of very poor quality; **tool:** sword, and a sexual pun

❓ **31** What is Gregory implying about Sampson?

33 marry: originally meant "Virgin Mary," but during this time period it was an exclamation comparable to "really," "indeed," etc.
35 list: please

36 bite my thumb: insulting gesture

PERSONA JOURNAL

How would your invented character react to these puns, insults, and sexual references?

41 of our side: on our side

✱ **The Fine Art of Thumb-Biting** Have you ever bitten your thumb at anyone? Probably not. But you're surely familiar with more up-to-date rude gestures, some of which have lost their sting from overuse. Perhaps it's time for thumb-biting to make a comeback. Here's how: put the end of your thumb between your teeth. Then yank your thumb forward, clicking the nail against your upper teeth. Done with the proper vigor, this gesture is sure to cause offense.

The taunting grows until a brawl breaks out. When Benvolio (a Montague) and Tybalt (a Capulet) enter, Benvolio tries to make peace. Tybalt, however, seems eager for a fight.

SAMPSON. *[To* ABRAHAM.*]* No, sir, I do not bite my thumb at you, sir; but I bite my thumb, sir.

GREGORY. *[To* ABRAHAM.*]* Do you quarrel, sir?   45

ABRAHAM. Quarrel, sir! no, sir.

SAMPSON. But if you do, sir, I am for you: I serve as good a man as you.

ABRAHAM. No better.

SAMPSON. Well, sir.   50

[Enter BENVOLIO.*]*

GREGORY. Say 'better'; here comes one of my master's kinsmen.

SAMPSON. *[To* ABRAHAM.*]* Yes, better, sir.

ABRAHAM. You lie.

SAMPSON. Draw, if you be men.—Gregory, remember thy swashing blow.   55

[They fight.]

BENVOLIO. Part, fools! put up your swords; you know not what you do.

[Beats down their swords.]

[Enter TYBALT.*]*

TYBALT. What, art thou drawn among these heartless hinds? Turn thee Benvolio, look upon thy death.

BENVOLIO. I do but keep the peace: put up thy sword,   60
Or manage it to part these men with me.

TYBALT. What, drawn, and talk of peace! I hate the word
As I hate hell, all Montagues, and thee:
Have at thee, coward!

[They fight.]

[Enter several of both Houses, who join the fray; then enter CITIZENS *with clubs.]*

47 am for you: I am ready to fight you.

? What happens to the boasts of the servants when they actually meet their rivals?

55 swashing: slashing sword blow

? How do Benvolio and Tybalt differ from one another?

58 Art . . . hinds: Are you fighting with these cowardly servants (**heartless hinds**)?

Citizens join the rioting, which becomes more and more heated. The Lords Capulet and Montague enter ready to do battle, but their wives restrain them.

A street fight suddenly breaks out. (Zeffirelli, 1968)

PERSONA ACTION

If you are in the square, join the brawl using stage fighting. You may also want to use your invented insults now, but remember that the audience needs to see and hear the main characters.

* **CITIZEN.** Clubs, bills, and partisans! Strike! Beat them down!   65
Down with the Capulets! Down with the Montagues!

[Enter CAPULET *in his gown and* LADY CAPULET.*]*

CAPULET. What noise is this?—Give me my long sword, ho!

LADY CAPULET. A crutch, a crutch!—Why call you for a sword?

CAPULET. My sword, I say!—Old Montague is come,
And flourishes his blade in spite of me.   70

[Enter MONTAGUE *and* LADY MONTAGUE.*]*

MONTAGUE. Thou villain Capulet!— Hold me not, let me go.

LADY MONTAGUE. Thou shalt not stir one foot to seek a foe.

65 bills, and partisans: long-handled weapons with blades

[*gown*] robe

68 A crutch, a crutch: Lady Capulet mocks her aged husband by suggesting that he needs a crutch, not a sword.

❓ How does the attitude of the wives differ from that of their husbands?

* **"Clubs, bills, and partisans!"**   This scene features an array of Renaissance weaponry, including a rapier—a lightweight, two-edged sword that had been invented fairly recently. Lord Capulet enters calling for his "long sword." Old-fashioned even then, this was a weighty, two-handed weapon with a blade about two inches wide and more than a yard long. As his wife suggests, Lord Capulet is probably too old to even lift it anymore.

Prince Escalus enters and commands that the fighting stop. With his patience strained, the Prince declares that if fighting erupts again, those who disturb the peace will die. All leave except the Montagues and Benvolio. Lord Montague asks Benvolio how the fight began.

[*Enter* PRINCE ESCALUS, *with* ATTENDANTS.]

✱ **PRINCE.** Rebellious subjects, enemies to peace,
Profaners of this neighbour-stainèd steel,—
Will they not hear?—What, ho! you men, you beasts,   75
That quench the fire of your pernicious rage
With purple fountains issuing from your veins,—
On pain of torture, from those bloody hands
Throw your mistemper'd weapons to the ground
And hear the sentence of your movèd prince.—   80
Three civil brawls, bred of an airy word,
By thee, old Capulet, and Montague,
Have thrice disturb'd the quiet of our streets;
And made Verona's ancient citizens
Cast by their grave beseeming ornaments,   85
To wield old partisans, in hands as old,
Canker'd with peace, to part your canker'd hate:
If ever you disturb our streets again,
Your lives shall pay the forfeit of the peace.
For this time, all the rest depart away:—   90
You, Capulet, shall go along with me;—
And, Montague, come you this afternoon,
To know our farther pleasure in this case,
To old Free-town, our common judgment-place.—
Once more, on pain of death, all men depart.   95

[*Exeunt* PRINCE *and* ATTENDANTS; CAPULET, LADY CAPULET, TYBALT, CITIZENS, *and* SERVANTS.]

MONTAGUE. Who set this ancient quarrel new abroach?—
Speak, nephew, were you by when it began?

(?) What mood is the Prince in? How might his voice and actions differ from others on the stage?

74 Profaners . . . steel: Those who misuse weapons stained with their neighbors' blood.
76 pernicious: destructive

79 mistemper'd: used for an evil purpose
80 moved: angry
81 airy word: careless or insulting remark

85–87 Cast by . . . hate: throw aside normal garb to carry weapons rusted (**Canker'd**) from disuse to stir up your malignant (**canker'd**) hate

89 forfeit of the peace: penalty for breaking the peace

93 farther pleasure: what else I have to say

(?) Who does the Prince blame for all the fighting? What warning does he give?

PERSONA JOURNAL

How did the events in the square affect you? Do you take sides?
96 abroach: opened

✱ **Family Feud** Shakespeare was a friend of the Earl of Southampton, whose neighbors, the Danvers and the Longs, had been feuding for at least 100 years. In 1594—possibly the year before *Romeo and Juliet* was written—this feud exploded into several murders. Because Shakespeare may have been in Southampton's home when the murders took place, he may have drawn on first-hand experience for the fight between the Capulets and Montagues.

Benvolio explains how the fight started. Lady Montague then asks if Benvolio has seen Romeo that day. Benvolio replies that he saw Romeo before daybreak, but that Romeo turned and went the other way, and Benvolio decided not to disturb him.

✱ **BENVOLIO.** Here were the servants of your adversary
    And yours, close fighting ere I did approach:
    I drew to part them: in the instant came   100
    The fiery Tybalt, with his sword prepar'd;
    Which, as he breath'd defiance to my ears,
    He swung about his head, and cut the winds,
    Who, nothing hurt withal, hiss'd him in scorn:
    While we were interchanging thrusts and blows,   105
    Came more and more, and fought on part and part,
    Till the prince came, who parted either part.

LADY MONTAGUE. O, where is Romeo?—saw you him to-day?—
    Right glad I am he was not at this fray.

BENVOLIO. Madam, an hour before the worshipp'd sun   110
    Peer'd forth the golden window of the east,
    A troubled mind drave me to walk abroad;
    Where,—underneath the grove of sycamore
    That westward rooteth from the city's side,—
    So early walking did I see your son: 115
    Towards him I made; but he was ware of me,
    And stole into the covert of the wood:
    I, measuring his affections by my own,—
    Which then most sought where most might not be found,
    Being one too many by my weary self,   120
    Pursu'd my humour, not pursuing his,
    And gladly shunn'd who gladly fled from me.

MONTAGUE. Many a morning hath he there been seen,
    With tears augmenting the fresh morning's dew,

98 adversary: enemy

100 drew: pulled out my weapon

104 withal: by this

112 drave: drove

114 rooteth: grows

116 ware: aware or wary
117 covert: cover
118–122 Benvolio explains that since neither he nor Romeo seemed to want company, he avoided (**shunn'd**) Romeo and left him to wander alone.

124 augmenting: adding to

✱ **"Here were the servants . . ."**   Benvolio describes events that we have already seen in order to answer Montague. But who wants to hear about things they already know? Inexperienced writers usually have trouble handling *exposition*—that is, working important information into a story. At thirty years of age, with only a few plays under his belt, Shakespeare did too. You'll find him struggling with this problem again, especially in the last scene of the play.

Lord Montague reveals that a tearful Romeo has been wandering all night and spending the day shut in his darkened room. The Montagues have no idea why Romeo is so depressed. Benvolio volunteers to find out.

Adding to clouds more clouds with his deep sighs: 125
But all so soon as the all-cheering sun
Should in the farthest east begin to draw
The shady curtains from Aurora's bed,
Away from light steals home my heavy son,
And private in his chamber pens himself;   130
Shuts up his windows, locks fair daylight out
And makes himself an artificial night:
* Black and portentous must this humour prove,
Unless good counsel may the cause remove.

BENVOLIO. My noble uncle, do you know the cause?   135

MONTAGUE. I neither know it nor can learn of him.

BENVOLIO. Have you importun'd him by any means?

MONTAGUE. Both by myself and many other friends;
But he, his own affections' counsellor,
Is to himself,—I will not say how true,—   140
But to himself so secret and so close,
So far from sounding and discovery,
As is the bud bit with an envious worm
Ere he can spread his sweet leaves to the air,
Or dedicate his beauty to the sun.   145
Could we but learn from whence his sorrows grow,
We would as willingly give cure as know.

[Enter ROMEO.*]*

BENVOLIO. See, where he comes: so please you step aside;
I'll know his grievance or be much denied.

128 Aurora: goddess of the dawn
129 heavy: sad
130 pens: secludes

133 portentous: ominous; **humour:** mood

137 importun'd: questioned

139–145 Montague says that Romeo keeps to himself, so it's difficult to discover what's troubling him. He's like a young bud ruined by an evil (**envious**) worm before it's had a chance to bloom.

? How would you describe Romeo's parents?

* **"Black and portentous must this humour prove . . ."**   In the Renaissance it was believed that human moods were caused by four fluids or "humours"—blood, phlegm, and yellow and black bile. The theory was that people's personalities depended on the mixture of these fluids. Blood made one optimistic; phlegm made one lazy; yellow bile made one angry; and black bile made one sad and melancholy. Here, Montague is worried that Romeo has too much black bile in his system.

Romeo enters and is greeted by Benvolio, who asks why he is so sad. Romeo, it seems, is in love, but his love is not returned.

MONTAGUE. I would thou wert so happy by thy stay   150
　　To hear true shrift.—Come, madam, let's away,

[Exeunt MONTAGUE *and* LADY MONTAGUE.*]*

BENVOLIO. Good morrow, cousin.

ROMEO.　　　　　　　　　　　　Is the day so young?

BENVOLIO. But new struck nine.

ROMEO.　　　　　　　　　Ay me! sad hours seem long.
　　Was that my father that went hence so fast?

BENVOLIO. It was.—What sadness lengthens Romeo's hours?   155

ROMEO. Not having that which, having, makes them short.

BENVOLIO. In love?

ROMEO. Out,—

BENVOLIO. Of love?

ROMEO. Out of her favour where I am in love.   160

BENVOLIO. Alas, that love, so gentle in his view,
　　Should be so tyrannous and rough in proof!

150–151 I hope you'll be lucky (**happy**) enough to hear a true confession (**shrift**) about what's bothering him.

PERSONA JOURNAL

Do you know Romeo? Have you noticed a difference in his behavior lately?

Benvolio sympathizes with Romeo, who replies that he is now doubly depressed since he must carry the weight of Benvolio's sympathy on top of the pain he already feels.

ROMEO. Alas that love, whose view is muffled still,
Should, without eyes, see pathways to his will!—
Where shall we dine?—O me!—What fray was here? 165
Yet tell me not, for I have heard it all.
Here's much to do with hate, but more with love:—
✱ Why, then, O brawling love! O loving hate!
O anything, of nothing first create!
O heavy lightness! serious vanity! 170
Mis-shapen chaos of well-seeming forms!
Feather of lead, bright smoke, cold fire, sick health!
Still-waking sleep, that is not what it is!—
This love feel I, that feel no love in this.
Dost thou not laugh?

BENVOLIO.　　No, coz, I rather weep. 175

ROMEO. Good heart, at what?

BENVOLIO.　　　　　At thy good heart's oppression.

ROMEO. Why, such is love's transgression.—
Griefs of mine own lie heavy in my breast;
Which thou wilt propagate, to have it prest
With more of thine: this love that thou hast shown 180
Doth add more grief to too much of mine own.
Love is a smoke rais'd with the fume of sighs;
Being purg'd, a fire sparkling in lovers' eyes;
Being vex'd, a sea nourish'd with lovers' tears:
What is it else? a madness most discreet, 185
A choking gall, and a preserving sweet.—
Farewell, my coz.

[Going.]

163 whose view is muffled still: whose eyes are always blindfolded. This is a reference to Cupid who is usually portrayed wearing a blindfold.
164 his will: amorous desire
165 fray: fight, disturbance

174 that feel no love in this: that can take no pleasure in this love

175 coz: cousin

179 wilt propagate: will increase; **prest:** burdened

182 fume: breath
183 Being purg'd: cleansed
184 vex'd: troubled

186 gall: bitterness

✱ **Oxymorons** Romeo here rattles off a string of word pairs that seem to have nothing to do with each other: "O heavy lightness! serious vanity!" etc. ("O anything, of nothing first create!" refers to an old saying, "Nothing can come of nothing.") When a writer puts a pair of contradictory words together like this, it is called an *oxymoron*. Oxymorons were common in love poetry of Shakespeare's time.

Benvolio asks Romeo to name his love, and Romeo rather foolishly replies that he is in love with—a woman!

BENVOLIO.   Soft! I will go along:
An if you leave me so, you do me wrong.

ROMEO. Tut! I have lost myself; I am not here:
This is not Romeo, he's some other where.   190

BENVOLIO. Tell me in sadness who is that you love?

ROMEO. What, shall I groan and tell thee?

BENVOLIO. Groan! why, no; But sadly tell me who.

ROMEO. Bid a sick man in sadness make his will,—
Ah, word ill urg'd to one that is so ill!—   195
In sadness, cousin, I do love a woman.

187 Soft: wait a minute

189 Tut: nonsense

191 sadness: seriousness

193 sadly: seriously

❓ How do you think the audience should relate to Romeo in this scene? As a sympathetic character? As foolish and overly-dramatic? How would his lines be read to achieve these reactions?

A Young Man Among Roses
Nicholas Hilliard, c. 1588

Romeo avoids disclosing the name of his love. He does, however, go on to describe her great beauty and to reveal that she has pledged to remain a virgin. Benvolio's advice is simple. He tells Romeo to forget her.

BENVOLIO. I aim'd so near when I suppos'd you lov'd.

ROMEO. A right good markman!—And she's fair I love.

BENVOLIO. A right fair mark, fair coz, is soonest hit.

ROMEO. Well, in that hit you miss: she'll not be hit   200
✱ With Cupid's arrow,—she hath Dian's wit;
And, in strong proof of chastity well arm'd,
From love's weak childish bow she lives unharm'd.
She will not stay the siege of loving terms
Nor bide th' encounter of assailing eyes,   205
Nor ope her lap to saint-seducing gold:
O, she's rich in beauty; only poor
That, when she dies, with beauty dies her store.

BENVOLIO. Then she hath sworn that she will still live chaste?

ROMEO. She hath, and in that sparing makes huge waste;   210
For beauty, starv'd with her severity,
Cuts beauty off from all posterity.
She is too fair, too wise; wisely too fair,
To merit bliss by making me despair:
She hath forsworn to love; and in that vow   215
Do I live dead that live to tell it now.

BENVOLIO. Be rul'd by me, forget to think of her.

ROMEO. O, teach me how I should forget to think.

BENVOLIO. By giving liberty unto thine eyes;
Examine other beauties.

201 Dian's wit: a reference to Diana, goddess of chastity, who avoided Cupid's arrows
202 proof: armor
204 stay: endure
204–206 Romeo's love refuses to be swayed by his affectionate words, his looks, or his money.
207–208 Her beauty is wasted, because it will never be passed on to any children.
209 still: forever

213–214 She is too fair . . . me despair: She's too beautiful and too wise. It's not right that her chastity should get her into heaven (**bliss**) while it makes me suffer.
215 forsworn to: sworn not to

❓ What kind of friend is Benvolio? What is his opinion of Romeo?

✱ **"With Cupid's arrow . . ."**   The Roman love god Cupid was originally the Greek deity Eros. In his earliest form, he was a handsome young man—and a lover himself, not unlike Romeo. But over the centuries, his image changed, and he became the winged baby we're more familiar with today. He was often portrayed as blindfolded, and carried a bow and arrow.

Benvolio suggests that Romeo think about other women, but Romeo says comparing his love to others will just make her seem more beautiful. Benvolio vows to change his mind.

ROMEO.   'Tis the way   220
    To call hers, exquisite, in question more:
    These happy masks that kiss fair ladies' brows,
    Being black, puts us in mind they hide the fair;
    He that is strucken blind cannot forget
    The precious treasure of his eyesight lost: 225
    Show me a mistress that is passing fair,
    What doth her beauty serve but as a note
    Where I may read who pass'd that passing fair?
    Farewell: thou canst not teach me to forget.

BENVOLIO. I'll pay that doctrine, or else die in debt.   230

    [Exeunt.]

220–221 'Tis the way . . . in question more: This would be just another way to remind me of her unparalleled beauty.
222 happy: fortunate; **masks:** masks were worn to protect female complexions from the sun.

226 passing: beyond
227 note: reminder
228 pass'd: surpassed

230 I'll pay that doctrine, or else die in debt: I'll convince you of that idea or die trying.

TALES FROM THE STAGE

Who was the worst actor ever to play Romeo? Theatre historians generally agree that it was Robert Coates (1772–1848). Although he had no talent, he was wealthy enough to finance his own productions. Actresses dreaded playing Juliet opposite him, for he was the frequent target of fruits, vegetables, and gales of laughter. During the scene in the Capulet's tomb, spectators sometimes called out to him, "Why don't you die?" The following is a review of one of his performances.

"On May 10th 1813, Mr. Coates appeared for the seventh time at the Haymarket Theatre in his old character of Romeo. We regret having to record that one of the most noisy houses assembled to witness this presentation, also to annoy and vex Mr. Coates. On the appearance of Mr. Coates upon the stage he was received by [the] band of rioters with crows and laughter. . . On the actors again appearing they were one and all pelted with orange peel by the members of this choice band of rioters, and thereupon made a sudden exit."

John R. and Hunter H. Robinson,
The Life of Robert Coates, 1891

Robert Coates, Esq. in the Character of Romeo,
Samuel de Wilde, 1812

Setting the Scene

ROMEO AND JULIET
Act I, scenes ii and iii *or* Will Juliet Go to Paris?

Critical Query: How do the attitudes and concerns
of the women in the play compare with those of the men?

Time Capsule

In a famous 14th-century epic called *The Divine Comedy*, Italian poet Dante briefly depicts the Montague and Capulet families as violent. This was more than 250 years before Shakespeare wrote *Romeo and Juliet*. Actually, the Montagues and Capulets never really fought against one another. They didn't even live in the same city. But the Cerchi and Donati families of Florence did feud, starting around 1300 and barely stopping for 50 years.

From the Prop Box

(for scene ii) a large scroll listing those who have been invited to the Capulet's party

In Character: Meet the Women

In scene iii you will meet the three main female characters of the play: Juliet, her mother, and her nurse. As you read the scene, think about how these characters differ from one another. Which one would be considered "bawdy"? Look up the word in a dictionary if you're not sure of its meaning.

Warm-up Improv 1	Warm-up Improv 2
You overhear two people discussing a party one of them is giving this weekend. As they talk about who's invited, you realize the love of your life will be there. With your friends, figure out how to crash the party.	Your mom and dad are going to visit friends they haven't seen in years. They insist that you go too, because their friends have a teenager just your age and "wouldn't it be wonderful if you two hit it off?"

Lord Capulet and Paris, a young nobleman, discuss a possible marriage between Paris and Juliet, Lord Capulet's daughter. Capulet is not opposed, but feels Juliet is still too young. He also wants Juliet's consent. Conversation shifts to the masked ball Capulet will host that evening.

Scene ii. A Street

[Enter CAPULET, PARIS, *and* SERVANT.*]*

CAPULET. But Montague is bound as well as I,
    In penalty alike; and 'tis not hard, I think,
    For men so old as we to keep the peace.

PARIS. Of honourable reckoning are you both;
    And pity 'tis you liv'd at odds so long.   5
    But now, my lord, what say you to my suit?

CAPULET. But saying o'er what I have said before:
    My child is yet a stranger in the world,
 ✷ She hath not seen the change of fourteen years;
    Let two more summers wither in their pride   10
    Ere we may think her ripe to be a bride.

PARIS. Younger than she are happy mothers made.

CAPULET. And too soon marr'd are those so early made.
    The earth hath swallow'd all my hopes but she,—
    She is the hopeful lady of my earth: 15
    But woo her, gentle Paris, get her heart,
    My will to her consent is but a part;
    An she agree, within her scope of choice
    Lies my consent and fair according voice.
    This night I hold an old accustom'd feast,   20
    Whereto I have invited many a guest,
    Such as I love; and you among the store,

PERSONA JOURNAL

What does your persona know about how the feud between the two families began.

1–2 bound . . . alike: We're both obligated (**bound**) by the threat (**penalty**) of death if we don't keep the peace.

4 reckoning: reputation

6 suit: marriage proposal

10 wither in their pride: pass by

14 the earth hath swallow'd all my hopes but she: She is my only living child.
15 hopeful lady: the child on whom all my hopes are pinned
17–19 My will . . . voice: My desire is only part of the decision. She needs to agree with the choice.

21 whereto: to which

22 store: group

? Why do you think Paris wants to marry Juliet?

✷ **"She hath not seen the change of fourteen years . . ."**   Are you surprised that Juliet isn't yet fourteen years old? In Elizabethan times, girls could legally marry as young as twelve. Early marriage was controversial, though, especially because of the dangers of childbirth. This may have been why Juliet's father says, "too soon marr'd are those so early made [mothers]." One writer of the time insisted that women shouldn't marry before turning eighteen. On the average, wealthy Elizabethan women married at twenty.

Lord Capulet suggests that Paris try to win Juliet's heart that evening at the banquet. Capulet then orders his servant, who has been walking along in attendance, to deliver the invitations. The servant cannot read and needs to find someone who can tell him what names are on the list.

One more, most welcome, makes my number more.
At my poor house look to behold this night
Earth-treading stars that make dark heaven light: 25
Such comfort as do lusty young men feel
When well apparell'd April on the heel
Of limping winter treads, even such delight
Among fresh female buds shall you this night
Inherit at my house; hear all, all see,   30
And like her most whose merit most shall be:
Which, among view of many, mine, being one,
May stand in number, though in reckoning none.
Come, go with me.—
    [To SERVANT, *giving him a paper]* Go, sirrah, trudge about
Through fair Verona; find those persons out   35
Whose names are written there, and to them say,
My house and welcome on their pleasure stay.

[Exeunt CAPULET *and* PARIS*].*

SERVANT. Find them out whose names are written here! It is
    written that the shoemaker should meddle with his yard and
    the tailor with his last, the fisher with his pencil, and the   40
    painter with his nets; but I am sent to find those persons
    whose names are here writ, and can never find what names
    the writing person hath here writ. I must to the learned:—in
    good time!

[Enter BENVOLIO *and* ROMEO*.]*

BENVOLIO. Tut, man, one fire burns out another's burning,   45
    One pain is lessen'd by another's anguish;
    Turn giddy, and be holp by backward turning;

25–33: You'll feel like spring has just arrived when you see all the lovely young women (**earth-treading stars**), (**fresh female buds**) invited to the banquet. You may choose someone other than Juliet after you've seen them all.

(?) What is your impression of Juliet's father?

34 sirrah: informal address to a servant or person of a lower class

(?) The servant is too embarrassed to let his master know that he cannot read. What else do you know about him from these lines? Is he witty or slow? comic or ordinary?

39–41 the shoemaker should . . . with his nets: The servant has mismatched workers and their materials. He means: the shoemaker's leather, the tailor's wool, the fisherman's nets, and the artist's pencil.
43–44 in good time: Here's help already.

47 holp: helped

Romeo and Benvolio greet the servant, who asks if Romeo can read. Romeo first teases the servant and then begins to read the list.

One desperate grief cures with another's languish:
Take thou some new infection to thy eye,
And the rank poison of the old will die.   50

50 rank: foul

❋ ROMEO. Your plantain-leaf is excellent for that.

BENVOLIO. For what, I pray thee?

ROMEO.   For your broken shin.

52 for your broken shin: implies that Romeo is about to kick Benvolio

BENVOLIO. Why, Romeo, art thou mad?

ROMEO. Not mad, but bound more than a madman is;
Shut up in prison, kept without my food,   55
Whipp'd and tormented and—God-den, good fellow.

56 God-den: good evening

SERVANT. God gi' go-den.—I pray, sir, can you read?

57 God gi' go-den: May God give you a good evening.

ROMEO. Ay, mine own fortune in my misery.

SERVANT. Perhaps you have learned it without book: but I pray,
can you read anything you see?   60

ROMEO. Ay, if I know the letters and the language.

SERVANT. Ye say honestly: rest you merry!

62 rest you merry: have a good day

ROMEO. Stay, fellow; I can read. [Reads.]
   'Signior Martino and his wife and daughters;
   County Anselmo and his beauteous sisters;   65
   The lady widow of Vitruvio;
   Signior Placentio and his lovely nieces;
   Mercutio and his brother Valentine;
   Mine uncle Capulet, his wife, and daughters;

65 County: Count

❋ **"Your plantain-leaf is excellent for that."** The leaves of the plantain plant are still used as medicine. They can be directly applied to wounds (including broken shins) and are also edible. Even today, some people believe the plantain to have magical powers. It is sometimes used to protect cars from evil spirits!

Romeo asks for details about the party. The servant responds and invites Romeo and Benvolio to attend, as long as they are not Montagues. Rosaline, the maiden Romeo loves, will be at the banquet. Benvolio wants him to compare her with the other young women who attend.

My fair niece Rosaline; Livia;   70
Signior Valentio and his cousin Tybalt;
Lucio and the lively Helena.'
A fair assembly. *[Gives back the paper]*: whither should they
   come?

SERVANT. Up.   75

ROMEO. Whither? To supper?

SERVANT. To our house.

ROMEO. Whose house?

SERVANT. My master's.

ROMEO. Indeed I should have ask'd you that before.   80

SERVANT. Now I'll tell you without asking: my master is the great
   rich Capulet; and if you be not of the house of Montagues, I
   pray, come and crush a cup of wine. Rest you merry!

[Exit.]

BENVOLIO. At this same ancient feast of Capulet's
   Sups the fair Rosaline whom thou so lov'st;   85
   With all the admirèd beauties of Verona.
   Go thither; and, with unattainted eye,
   Compare her face with some that I shall show,
   And I will make thee think thy swan a crow.

ROMEO. When the devout religion of mine eye   90
   Maintains such falsehood, then turn tears to fires;
   And these,—who, often drown'd, could never die,—
   Transparent heretics, be burnt for liars!
   One fairer than my love? the all-seeing sun

? Rosaline, the object of Romeo's affection, is Capulet's niece. This is the first time her name is mentioned in the play. How might Romeo react when her name is read?

PERSONA JOURNAL

The invitation list is very long. Is your name on it? Why or why not?

83 crush: drink

87 thither: there; **unattainted:** unbiased

90–93 When . . . liars: My tears would turn to fire and burn my deceitful eyes (**transparent heretics**) if my love for Rosaline ever changed.

Romeo doubts that anyone could compare with Rosaline, but agrees to go in order to prove that she is indeed the most beautiful of all women.

Ne'er saw her match since first the world begun.   95

BENVOLIO. Tut, you saw her fair, none else being by,
    Herself pois'd with herself in either eye:
    But in that crystal scales let there be weigh'd
    Your lady's love against some other maid
    That I will show you shining at this feast,   100
    And she shall scant show well that now seems best.

ROMEO. I'll go along, no such sight to be shown,
    But to rejoice in splendour of my own.

[Exeunt.]

97 pois'd: compared

❓ What else might Benvolio say or do to convince Romeo that he should forget about Rosaline?

103 splendour of my own: the beauty of my Rosaline

The scene takes place in the Capulet house where Lady Capulet has requested Juliet's presence. Lady Capulet, who seems ill at ease, first asks the Nurse to leave, then changes her mind. Next, she asks the Nurse to confirm Juliet's age.

❋   Scene iii. A Room in Capulet's House

[Enter LADY CAPULET *and* NURSE.*]*

LADY CAPULET. Nurse, where's my daughter? call her forth to me.

NURSE. Now, by my maidenhead,—at twelve year old,—
I bade her come.—What, lamb! what ladybird!—
God forbid!—where's this girl?—what, Juliet!

3 bade: asked

[Enter JULIET.*]*

JULIET. How now, who calls?

NURSE.   Your mother.   5

JULIET. Madam, I am here. What is your will?

LADY CAPULET. This is the matter,—Nurse, give leave awhile,
We must talk in secret: nurse, come back again;
I have remember'd me, thou's hear our counsel.
Thou knowest my daughter's of a pretty age.   10

7 give leave awhile: please leave us

9 thou's: thou shalt

10 a pretty age: of marrying age

NURSE. Faith, I can tell her age unto an hour.

LADY CAPULET. She's not fourteen.

NURSE.   I'll lay fourteen of my teeth,—
And yet, to my teen be it spoken, I have but four,—
She is not fourteen. How long is it now
To Lammas-tide?

13 teen: sorrow

LADY CAPULET.   A fortnight and odd days.   15

15 Lammas-tide: August 1, a holy feast day

A View of the City of London,
1616

❋ **I See London . . .**   Why didn't Shakespeare set any of his plays in London? Many agree with Shakespeare scholar and actor Peter O'Toole, who insists, "*All* his plays are set in London." Because Shakespeare had little concern for period or locale, the Capulets seem more like London merchants than Italian aristocrats. In other plays, Shakespeare even dressed Greeks and Romans in the latest London fashions.

The Nurse gets carried away with reminiscing about Juliet's birth and childhood years. She goes on to tell a crude sexual joke.

NURSE. Even or odd, of all days in the year,
    Come Lammas-eve at night shall she be fourteen.
    Susan and she,—God rest all Christian souls!—
    Were of an age: well, Susan is with God;
    She was too good for me:—but, as I said,   20
    On Lammas-eve at night shall she be fourteen;
    That shall she, marry; I remember it well.
 ❋ 'Tis since the earthquake now eleven years;
    And she was wean'd,—I never shall forget it—,
    Of all the days of the year, upon that day: 25
    For I had then laid wormwood to my dug,
    Sitting in the sun under the dove-house wall;
    My lord and you were then at Mantua:
    Nay, I do bear a brain:—but, as I said,
    When it did taste the wormwood on the nipple   30
    Of my dug and felt it bitter, pretty fool,
    To see it tetchy, and fall out with the dug!
    'Shake,' quoth the dove-house: 'twas no need, I trow,
    To bid me trudge.
    And since that time it is eleven years;   35
    For then she could stand alone; nay, by the rood
    She could have run and waddled all about;
    For even the day before, she broke her brow:
    And then my husband,—God be with his soul!
    'A was a merry man,—took up the child: 40
    'Yea,' quoth he, 'dost thou fall upon thy face?
    Thou wilt fall backward when thou hast more wit;
    Wilt thou not, Jule?' and, by my holidame,
    The pretty wretch left crying, and said 'Ay:'

16–48 The Nurse now recalls Juliet's childhood and her own daughter, Susan, who was the same age.

22 marry: I swear

24 wean'd: stopped breast-feeding

26 laid . . . dug: rubbed a bitter-tasting plant (**wormwood**) on my breast (**dug**) to discourage the child from breast-feeding
29 I do bear a brain: I have a good memory.

32 tetchy: fretful, peevish

33–34 Shake . . . trudge: I declare, (**trow**) no one needed to tell me to leave (**trudge**) the dove-house when it shook during the earthquake.
36 rood: cross

38 even: just; **broke her brow:** cut her forehead
39–44: To stop the baby from crying after her fall, the Nurse's husband makes a bawdy joke. He asks if Juliet will fall the other way (**backward**) when she's older. Though not understanding, Juliet stops fussing and answers, "Yes." The Nurse finds this so funny that she can't stop laughing about it.
43 by my holidame: a mild oath referring to the "holy dame" or Virgin Mary

---

❋ **" 'Tis since the earthquake now eleven years . . ."** There were earthquakes in England in 1570 and 1584. Might the Nurse be referring to one of them in her speech? Back when scholars didn't know in what year Shakespeare wrote *Romeo and Juliet*, they tried to date the play by the years earthquakes occurred. Ultimately they used other clues to decide that Shakespeare wrote *Romeo and Juliet* around 1595. That date would correspond to the English earthquake of 1584.

Lady Capulet tries to quiet the Nurse, who continues to elaborate on the joke. Finally, Juliet, too, asks the Nurse to stop.

To see now how a jest shall come about!   45
I warrant, an I should live a thousand years,
I never should forget it; 'Wilt thou not, Jule?' quoth he;
And, pretty fool, it stinted, and said 'Ay.'

LADY CAPULET. Enough of this; I pray thee hold thy peace.

NURSE. Yes, madam;—yet I cannot choose but laugh,   50
To think it should leave crying, and say 'Ay:'
And yet, I warrant, it had upon its brow
A bump as big as a young cockerel's stone;
A parlous knock; and it cried bitterly.
'Yea,' quoth my husband, 'fall'st upon thy face?   55
Thou wilt fall backward when thou com'st to age;
Wilt thou not, Jule?' it stinted, and said 'Ay.'

JULIET. And stint thou too, I pray thee, nurse, say I.

46 warrant: swear

48 stinted: stopped

53 cockerel's stone: rooster's testicle
54 parlous knock: severe blow

❓ How do you think Juliet would act towards her mother? towards the Nurse?

A performance of *Romeo and Juliet* at the Open Air Theatre in London's Regent's Park

The Nurse states her wish to see Juliet wed, which is the subject Lady Capulet has been trying to introduce. She tells Juliet that Paris has asked for her hand. Both Lady Capulet and the Nurse begin to list his fine qualities.

NURSE. Peace, I have done. God mark thee to his grace!
    Thou wast the prettiest babe that e'er I nurs'd: 60
    An I might live to see thee married once,
    I have my wish.

LADY CAPULET. Marry, that 'marry' is the very theme
    I came to talk of.—Tell me, daughter Juliet,
    How stands your disposition to be married?   65

JULIET. It is an honour that I dream not of.

NURSE. An honour!—were not I thine only nurse,
    I would say thou hadst suck'd wisdom from thy teat.

LADY CAPULET. Well, think of marriage now: younger than you,
    Here in Verona, ladies of esteem,   70
    Are made already mothers: by my count
    I was your mother much upon these years
    That you are now a maid. Thus, then, in brief;—
    The valiant Paris seeks you for his love.

NURSE. A man, young lady! lady, such a man   75
    As all the world—why he's a man of wax.

LADY CAPULET. Verona's summer hath not such a flower.

NURSE. Nay, he's a flower, in faith, a very flower.

LADY CAPULET. What say you? can you love the gentleman?
    This night you shall behold him at our feast;   80
    Read o'er the volume of young Paris' face,
    And find delight writ there with beauty's pen;
    Examine every married lineament,

63 Explain the two ways the word "marry" is used in this sentence.

72 much upon these years: at about the same age as you are now

PERSONA JOURNAL

Would you be in favor of a marriage between Paris and Juliet? Why or why not?

76 a man of wax: a perfect specimen of a man (like a sculptor's wax model)

81–94 In this extended metaphor, Paris is compared to a book. How many "book" references can you find?

83 every married lineament: each different feature

How do you think Juliet might feel about the idea of marriage?

Lady Capulet and the Nurse continue to compliment Paris, and Juliet agrees to give his suit favorable consideration. At this point a servant announces that guests have arrived for the banquet.

And see how one another lends content;
And what obscur'd in this fair volume lies   85
Find written in the margent of his eyes.
This precious book of love, this unbound lover,
To beautify him, only lacks a cover:
The fish lives in the sea; and 'tis much pride
For fair without the fair within to hide: 90
That book in many's eyes doth share the glory,
That in gold clasps locks in the golden story;
So shall you share all that he doth possess,
By having him, making yourself no less.

NURSE. No less! nay, bigger; women grow by men.   95

LADY CAPULET. Speak briefly, can you like of Paris' love?

JULIET. I'll look to like, if looking liking move:
But no more deep will I endart mine eye
Than your consent gives strength to make it fly.

[Enter a SERVANT.]

SERVANT. Madam, the guests are come, supper served up, you   100
called, my young lady asked for, the nurse cursed in the
pantry, and everything in extremity. I must hence to wait; I
beseech you, follow straight.

✱ **LADY CAPULET.** We follow thee. Juliet, the County stays.

NURSE. Go, girl, seek happy nights to happy days.   105

[Exeunt.]

84 one another lends content: one feature compliments another
85–86 what obscur'd . . . of his eyes: and to see his inner qualities, just look into his eyes; **margent:** margin notes in books
88 lacks a cover: A wife would make him more handsome.
89–90 the fish lives . . . within to hide: The fish lives in the sea, and it's wonderful that something beautiful is hidden in something else that is beautiful.

? **95** What does the Nurse mean by this bawdy pun?

97 I'll look to . . . move: I will look at him and like him, if looking can make liking happen.
98 endart: shoot as a dart

102 extremity: confusion

104 the County stays: The Count is waiting for you.

PERSONA JOURNAL

Assume that you know one of the three women in this scene. How do you know her, and what is your opinion of her?

✱ **Getting to Know Thee**   By this point in the play, you're probably comfortable with Shakespeare's use of "thou" and "thee." Have you noticed that he uses "you" more often than he does those old-fashioned words? By Shakespeare's time, "thou" and "thee" were starting to disappear from the language.

Setting the Scene

ROMEO AND JULIET

Act I, scene iv *or* I Had the Strangest Dream

Critical Query: What purposes do dreams serve in this scene?

Classroom Set Design

Create a winding street through the classroom by pushing desks out of the way. Make the room as dark as possible so that the flashlights that will be used seem more like torches.

Desk	Acting Area

Street

From the Prop Box

- Flashlights to be used as torches
- Masks for the people in this scene who are on their way to the party

Word Play: Are We Having Puns Yet?

A pun is a humorous play on words such as the title above, where the expected word "fun" is replaced by the word "puns." Shakespeare obviously loved puns. His plays are filled with them, and certain scenes such as the one you are about to read are virtual word wars where each character tries to outdo the other with outrageous and often sexual references. The most common varieties of puns make use of words with multiple meanings (fume, case, grate), or words with different spellings that sound alike (soul/sole, pair/pare, hair/hare).

Warm-up Improv: Just Dreamy

Your friend has a problem and is feeling depressed. Try to distract him or her by telling about a dream you had the previous night. The dream was very long and filled with fantastic details.

Time Capsule: Interpretation of Dreams

Dreams have been a source of prophecy for centuries. Interpreting a dream's message even got the Old Testament's Joseph out of an Egyptian jail. Since the Renaissance was a highly superstitious time with strong beliefs in astrology and other omens, it is not surprising that using dreams to predict future events was taken quite seriously. Today, many believe that dreams contain symbols which can be interpreted to reveal unconscious fears and desires.

Romeo, Benvolio, and Mercutio (their good friend and a relative of the prince) walk towards the Capulet house discussing how best to crash the party. Since it is a masquerade, they are all in disguise. Mercutio tries to cheer up Romeo by telling jokes.

Scene iv. A Street

✱ *[Enter* ROMEO, MERCUTIO, BENVOLIO, *with five or six Maskers; Torch-bearers, and others.]*

ROMEO. What, shall this speech be spoke for our excuse?
Or shall we on without apology?

BENVOLIO. The date is out of such prolixity:
We'll have no Cupid hoodwink'd with a scarf,
Bearing a Tartar's painted bow of lath,   5
Scaring the ladies like a crow-keeper;
Nor no without-book prologue, faintly spoke
After the prompter, for our entrance:
But, let them measure us by what they will,
We'll measure them a measure, and be gone.   10

ROMEO. Give me a torch,—I am not for this ambling;
Being but heavy, I will bear the light.

MERCUTIO. Nay, gentle Romeo, we must have you dance.

ROMEO. Not I, believe me: you have dancing shoes,
With nimble soles; I have a soul of lead   15
So stakes me to the ground I cannot move.

MERCUTIO. You are a lover; borrow Cupid's wings,
And soar with them above a common bound.

PERSONA ACTION

Ten or so men loyal to the Capulets enter with the speaking characters. Some wear masks and/or carry torches.

1–2 shall this speech . . . without apology: Shall I send someone to formally introduce us, or shall we just enter without an introduction?

3–8 The date . . . be gone: This elaborate custom (**prolixity**) is outdated. We won't send someone costumed as a blindfolded (**hoodwinked**) Cupid to announce us and frighten people like a scarecrow (**crow-keeper**) would. The hosts need to accept us as we are. We'll dance one dance (**measure**) and leave.

❓ Do you think Romeo is nervous about crashing this party? Explain.

12 heavy: sad

15 sole/soul: Romeo may be sad, but he still keeps making puns.

18 bound: leap

✱ **Uninvited Guests**   As they enter, Romeo and his friends are going to the Capulets' masquerade—a party where guests wore masks and disguises. The anonymity of a masked ball encouraged flirtation—a bit like today's Internet chat rooms. Note that Mercutio has been invited to the ball, but Romeo and Benvolio have not. Today we might call them "gatecrashers," but in the Renaissance, the host of a masked ball felt honored when unexpected guests arrived.

Romeo and Mercutio continue to banter back and forth. Benvolio wants everyone to dance at the party, but Romeo insists that he will just hold a torch and watch.

ROMEO. I am too sore enpiercèd with his shaft
 To soar with his light feathers; and so bound,   20
 I cannot bound a pitch above dull woe:
 Under love's heavy burden do I sink.

MERCUTIO. And, to sink in it, should you burden love;
 Too great oppression for a tender thing.

ROMEO. Is love a tender thing? it is too rough,   25
 Too rude, too boisterous; and it pricks like thorn.

MERCUTIO. If love be rough with you, be rough with love;
 Prick love for pricking, and you beat love down.—
 Give me a case to put my visage in: *[Putting on a mask.]*
 A visard for a visard! what care I   30
 What curious eye doth quote deformities?
 Here are the beetle-brows shall blush for me.

BENVOLIO. Come, knock and enter; and no sooner in
 But every man betake him to his legs.

ROMEO. A torch for me: let wantons, light of heart,   35
✱ Tickle the senseless rushes with their heels;
 For I am proverb'd with a grandsire phrase,—
 I'll be a candle-holder and look on,—
 The game was ne'er so fair, and I am done.

MERCUTIO. Tut, dun's the mouse, the constable's own word: 40
 If thou art dun, we'll draw thee from the mire
 Of this—save your reverence—love, wherein thou stick'st
 Up to the ears.—Come, we burn daylight, ho.

21 bound a pitch: leap any distance at all

29 give me a case to put my visage in: Give me a mask to cover my face.
30 a visard for a visard: a mask for an ugly face
31 curious: careful; **quote:** report
32 beetle-brows: beetle-like eyebrows on the mask
34 betake him to his legs: dance

35 a torch for me: a pun on carrying a torch for Rosaline; **wantons:** mischievous men
37 proverb'd with a grandsire phrase: counseled by an old proverb

40–41 Tut, dun's the mouse . . . from the mire: Mercutio makes a number of puns on the words "done" and "dun": the proverb "dun's the mouse" (keep quiet), and a game entitled "dun is in the mire" (a horse is stuck in the mud).
42 save your reverence: beg your pardon
43 burn daylight: waste time

✱ **" . . . Tickle the senseless rushes . . ."**   In the time of this play, floors were seldom clean. Often they were littered with straw and layer upon layer of dried plants called rushes, used to cover dirt and spilt food. Although mixed with sweet-smelling herbs, rushes smelled quite awful after a while, and insects and rodents made their homes among them. But rushes did make floors softer for servants to sleep on. To "tickle the senseless rushes with one's heels" means to dance.

Mercutio tries to hurry the group along, but Romeo is hesitant because of a bad dream he had the previous night. Mercutio scoffs at the idea and proceeds to deliver a fantastic speech about Queen Mab, a fairy queen who delivers strange dreams to mankind.

ROMEO. Nay, that's not so.

MERCUTIO.   I mean, sir, in delay
We waste our lights in vain, like lamps by day.   45
Take our good meaning, for our judgment sits
Five times in that ere once in our five wits.

44–47 While we're stalling, we're using up our torches (**lights**). You know what I meant to say (**good meaning**).

ROMEO. And we mean well, in going to this mask;
But 'tis no wit to go.

48 And: Although

MERCUTIO.   Why, may one ask?

49 no wit: not a good idea

ROMEO. I dreamt a dream to-night.

MERCUTIO.   And so did I.   50

50 to-night: last night

ROMEO. Well, what was yours?

MERCUTIO.   That dreamers often lie.

ROMEO. In bed asleep, while they do dream things true.

✱ **MERCUTIO.** O, then, I see Queen Mab hath been with you.
She is the fairies' midwife; and she comes
In shape no bigger than an agate-stone   55
On the fore-finger of an alderman,
Drawn with a team of little atomies
Athwart men's noses as they lie asleep:
Her waggon-spokes made of long spinners' legs;
The cover, of the wings of grasshoppers;   60
The traces, of the smallest spider's web;
The collars, of the moonshine's watery beams;

57 atomies: miniature beings

59 spinners: spiders

61 traces: harness

✱ **". . . I see Queen Mab hath been with you."**   Here, Mercutio delivers one of the most famous speeches in *Romeo and Juliet*—and yet it seems to have nothing to do with the story! Why does Mercutio rant on and on about Queen Mab for forty-two lines, until Romeo finally shuts him up? Some scholars think Shakespeare may have written this speech before writing *Romeo and Juliet*, and didn't know what to do with it. Perhaps he put it in Mercutio's mouth just to find some use for it.

Her whip, of cricket's bone; the lash, of film;
Her waggoner, a small grey-coated gnat,
Not half so big as a round little worm   65
Prick'd from the lazy finger of a maid:
Her chariot is an empty hazel-nut,
Made by the joiner squirrel or old grub,
Time out o' mind the fairies' coachmakers.
And in this state she gallops night by night   70
Through lovers' brains, and then they dream of love;
O'er courtiers' knees, that dream on court'sies straight;
O'er lawyers' fingers, who straight dream on fees;
O'er ladies' lips, who straight on kisses dream,—
Which oft the angry Mab with blisters plagues,   75
Because their breaths with sweetmeats tainted are:
Sometime she gallops o'er a courtier's nose,
And then dreams he of smelling out a suit;
And sometime comes she with a tithe-pig's tail,
Tickling a parson's nose as 'a lies asleep,   80
Then dreams he of another benefice:
Sometime she driveth o'er a soldier's neck,
And then dreams he of cutting foreign throats,
Of breaches, ambuscadoes, Spanish blades,
Of healths five fathom deep; and then anon   85
Drums in his ear, at which he starts and wakes;
And, being thus frighted, swears a prayer or two,
And sleeps again. This is that very Mab
That plaits the manes of horses in the night;
And bakes the elf-locks in foul sluttish hairs, 90
Which, once untangled, much misfortune bodes:
This is the hag, when maids lie on their backs,

65–66 little worm . . . maid: Lazy maids were thought to grow maggots in their fingers.

68 joiner: carpenter

72 court'sies: bowing

78 smelling out a suit: being paid to influence the court
79 tithe-pig: a pig given to a church as a tithe
81 benefice: high-paying job

84 ambuscadoes: ambushes
85 healths: toasts to one's good health

89 plaits: braids
90 elf-locks: when dirty hair became tangled it was attributed to the elves
92 hag: nightmare

Romeo begs Mercutio to stop his rambling. Mercutio repeats his belief that dreams are nothing but foolish fantasy. Romeo, however, is still worried about his dream and believes that it is a bad omen.

That presses them, and learns them first to bear,
Making them women of good carriage:
This is she,—

ROMEO.   Peace, peace, Mercutio, peace,   95
Thou talk'st of nothing.

✳ **MERCUTIO.**   True, I talk of dreams,
Which are the children of an idle brain,
Begot of nothing but vain fantasy;
Which is as thin of substance as the air,
And more inconstant than the wind, who woos   100
Even now the frozen bosom of the north,
And, being anger'd, puffs away from thence,
Turning his face to the dew-dropping south.

BENVOLIO. This wind you talk of blows us from ourselves:
Supper is done, and we shall come too late.   105

ROMEO. I fear, too early: for my mind misgives
Some consequence, yet hanging in the stars,
Shall bitterly begin his fearful date
With this night's revels; and expire the term
Of a despisèd life, clos'd in my breast,   110
By some vile forfeit of untimely death:
But He that hath the steerage of my course
Direct my sail!—On, lusty gentlemen!

BENVOLIO. Strike, drum.

[Exeunt.]

93 women of good carriage: women who bear children well

98 begot: born

100 inconstant: changeable

103 dew-dropping south: the rainy south wind
104 the wind you . . . from ourselves: implies that Mercutio is long winded and talks too much
106–111 I fear . . . death: I fear some terrible tragedy will begin tonight and end with my death.
107 consequence: event to come
108 his: its

113 lusty gentlemen: my fine gentlemen

✳ **Unrivaled**   Early on, Shakespeare's great rival was playwright Christopher Marlowe (1564–1593). Like Mercutio, Marlowe had a reputation for being "mercurial"—that is, moody, passionate, and wild. During his short, adventurous life, Marlowe served as an English spy. He died just before Shakespeare wrote *Romeo and Juliet*, stabbed in the eye during a tavern fight. Some scholars believe that Shakespeare modeled Mercutio on his late friend and rival.

Setting the Scene

ROMEO AND JULIET
Act I, scene v *or* Love at First Sight

Critical Query: What conflicts are set in motion by events in this scene?

From the Prop Box

- Masks for partygoers as well as other costume items
- Aprons and napkins for the servants

Classroom Set Design

As the scene begins, desks are pushed out of the way by Capulet servants to allow as much room as possible for guests. A few chairs should be scattered around the acting area as seating for "older" guests.

```
Desk      ☐  ☐
          Dance and        ☐
          Acting Space
                            ◇
Entrance

☐ ☐ ☐ ☐ ☐ ☐ ☐ ☐
☐ ☐ ☐ ☐ ☐ ☐ ☐
```

Special Effects: Music and Dance

Play recorded Renaissance music in the background; bring up volume during the dance. Or invite student musicians to play during the scene. Learn a simple Renaissance dance sequence or have student dancers perform for or teach the class.

In Character: Tempestuous Tybalt

What do you learn about Tybalt from this scene?

Warm-up Improv: Forbidden Love

Your friends dragged you along to a basketball game at a rival school. At halftime, you glimpse the most gorgeous person you've ever seen. Your eyes meet and you fight through the mob to get to each other. Some breathless flirting occurs and then halftime is over. Your newfound love disappears and only then do you learn that he/she is . . . (make up anyone you absolutely should NOT fall in love with)!

As the scene begins, the servants are clearing away leftover food and furniture from a hall in the Capulet house in order to prepare the room for dancing. The guests enter the hall. Lord Capulet greets them and encourages them to dance.

Scene v. A Hall in Capulet's House

[MUSICIANS waiting. Enter SERVANTS with napkins.]

1 SERVANT. Where's Potpan, that he helps not to take away? He shift a trencher? He scrape a trencher?

2 SERVANT. When good manners shall lie all in one or two men's hands, and they unwash'd too, 'tis a foul thing.

1 SERVANT. Away with the join-stools, remove the court-cupboard, look to the plate:—good thou, save me a piece of marchpane; and as thou loves me, let the porter let in Susan Grindstone and Nell.—Antony! and Potpan!

3 SERVANT. Ay, boy, ready.

1 SERVANT. You are looked for and called for, asked for and sought for in the great chamber.

4 SERVANT. We cannot be here and there too.—Cheerly, boys; be brisk awhile, and the longer liver take all.

[Exeunt.]

[Enter CAPULET, LADY CAPULET, JULIET, TYBALT, NURSE, and all the GUESTS and GENTLEWOMEN, meeting the MASKERS.]

CAPULET. Welcome, gentlemen! ladies that have their toes
Unplagu'd with corns will have a bout with you.—
Ah ha, my mistresses! which of you all
Will now deny to dance? she that makes dainty, she,
I'll swear hath corns; am I come near you now?

[Enter ROMEO, BENVOLIO, and MERCUTIO.]

Welcome, gentlemen! I have seen the day
That I have worn a visard; and could tell
A whispering tale in a fair lady's ear,
Such as would please;—'tis gone, 'tis gone, 'tis gone:

1–2 The lines imply that Potpan is never around when there's work to be done.
2 trencher: a wooden plate

5 join-stools: folding stools; **court-cupboard:** sideboard
6 marchpane: marzipan, a sweet paste made from almonds

15 bout: dance

17 makes dainty: pretends to be shy

18 am I come near you now: Is this joke hitting close to home?

20 visard: mask

PERSONA ACTION

If you work for the Capulets you will need to clear away the dinner and move furniture so that dancing can take place. Everyone else except the Montagues and their servants will be guests at the party.

Capulet commands the musicians to play, gives orders to the servants, and then reminisces about the past. Romeo sees Juliet for the first time.

You are welcome, gentlemen!—Come, musicians, play.
A hall—a hall! give room! and foot it, girls.—

[Music plays, and they dance.]

More light, you knaves; and turn the tables up,   25
✱ And quench the fire, the room is grown too hot.—
Ah, sirrah, this unlook'd-for sport comes well.
Nay, sit, nay, sit, good cousin Capulet;
For you and I are past our dancing days;
How long is't now since last yourself and I   30
Were in a mask?

2 CAPULET.   By'r Lady, thirty years.

CAPULET. What, man! 'tis not so much, 'tis not so much:
'Tis since the nuptial of Lucentio,
Come Pentecost as quickly as it will,
Some five-and-twenty years; and then we mask'd.   35

2 CAPULET. 'Tis more, 'tis more: his son is elder, sir;
His son is thirty.

CAPULET.   Will you tell me that?
His son was but a ward two years ago.

ROMEO *[To a* SERVANT*]*. What lady is that, which doth enrich the hand
Of yonder knight?   40

SERVANT. I know not, sir.

---

24 a hall: make the room ready for dancing

PERSONA ACTION

Many people dance. Others clap and call out to the dancers.

25 knaves: rascals; **turn the tables up:** move the tables out of the way
27 this unlook'd for sport: the arrival of uninvited guests
28 cousin: any relative

31 By'r Lady: By our lady/Virgin Mary

36 elder: older than twenty-five years

38 ward: minor

❓ What has Romeo been doing at the party so far? Does he dance? Talk to other guests? How do his actions change when he sees Juliet?

✱ **Senior Moment?** Do you remember when Lady Capulet remarked that Lammas-tide was a little more that two weeks away (page 41, line 15)? This clearly sets the play during July. And indeed, the atmosphere of *Romeo and Juliet* generally seems summery. So why does Capulet ask his servants to "quench the fire"? Shakespeare seems to have forgotten the season of his play! Never a stickler for consistency, he made little mistakes like this even late in his career.

Romeo is overwhelmed by Juliet's beauty and instantly forgets about his love for Rosaline.

ROMEO. O, she doth teach the torches to burn bright!
It seems she hangs upon the cheek of night
Like a rich jewel in an Ethiop's ear;
Beauty too rich for use, for earth too dear!   45
So shows a snowy dove trooping with crows
As yonder lady o'er her fellows shows.
The measure done, I'll watch her place of stand
And, touching hers, make blessèd my rude hand.
Did my heart love till now? forswear it, sight!   50
For I ne'er saw true beauty till this night.

44 Ethiop: a person of African heritage

❓ Notice Romeo's words and his use of light images as he refers to Juliet. Why do you think he chooses these words?

48–49 The measure . . . hand: When the dance is over, Romeo will find Juliet and "bless" his hand by touching hers.

❓ Do you think it's possible to fall in and out of love as quickly as Romeo does?

PERSONA JOURNAL

How would you feel about a romance and possible marriage between Romeo and Juliet?

Romeo sees Juliet for the first time. (Zeffirelli, 1968)

Tybalt recognizes Romeo and is furious that he has dared to crash a Capulet party. He alerts Lord Capulet to Romeo's presence, but Capulet refuses to be upset. He does not want a disturbance in his house and has heard that Romeo is a well-mannered young man.

TYBALT. This, by his voice, should be a Montague.
　　Fetch me my rapier, boy:—what, dares the slave
　　Come hither, cover'd with an antic face,
　　To fleer and scorn at our solemnity? 55
　　Now, by the stock and honour of my kin,
　　To strike him dead I hold it not a sin.

CAPULET. Why, how now, kinsman! wherefore storm you so?

TYBALT. Uncle, this is a Montague, our foe;
　　A villain, that is hither come in spite, 60
　　To scorn at our solemnity this night.

CAPULET. Young Romeo, is it?

TYBALT.　　　　　　　　　'Tis he, that villain, Romeo.

CAPULET. Content thee, gentle coz, let him alone,
　　He bears him like a portly gentleman;
　　And, to say truth, Verona brags of him 65
　　To be a virtuous and well-govern'd youth:
　　I would not for the wealth of all the town
　　Here in my house do him disparagement:
　　Therefore be patient, take no note of him,—
　　It is my will; the which if thou respect, 70
　　Show a fair presence and put off these frowns,
　　An ill-beseeming semblance for a feast.

52 **should:** must
53 **rapier:** sword
54 **antic face:** grotesque mask
55 **fleer:** jeer; **solemnity:** festivity

? What makes Tybalt so angry?

63 **coz:** nephew
64 **portly:** dignified

? Why is Lord Capulet not offended by Romeo's presence at the party?

71 **show a fair presence:** put a good face on it
72 **ill-beseeming semblance:** unbecoming appearance

PERSONA JOURNAL

Suppose you overheard the conversation between Tybalt and Capulet on this and the following page. Whose side would you be on? Why?

Tybalt continues to rant. Lord Capulet loses his patience and orders Tybalt to leave Romeo alone. Tybalt storms out in a rage and vows to avenge what he sees as Romeo's insulting behavior. Romeo speaks to Juliet.

TYBALT. It fits, when such a villain is a guest:
　　I'll not endure him.

CAPULET.　　　　　　　　He shall be endur'd:
　　What, goodman boy!—I say he shall;—go to;　　　　　75
　　Am I the master here, or you? go to.
　　You'll not endure him!—God shall mend my soul,
　　You'll make a mutiny among my guests!
　　You will set cock-a-hoop! you'll be the man!

TYBALT. Why, uncle, 'tis a shame.

CAPULET.　　　　　　　　　　Go to, go to!　　　　　80
　　You are a saucy boy. Is't so, indeed?—
　　This trick may chance to scathe you,—I know what:
　　You must contrary me! marry, 'tis time.—
　　Well said, my hearts!—You are a princox; go:
　　Be quiet, or—More light, more light!—For shame!　　　85
　　I'll make you quiet. What!—cheerly, my hearts.

TYBALT. Patience perforce with wilful choler meeting
　　Makes my flesh tremble in their different greeting.
　　I will withdraw: but this intrusion shall,
　　Now seeming sweet, convert to bitter gall.　　　　　90

[Exit.]

✱ **ROMEO.** *[To* JULIET.*]* If I profane with my unworthiest hand
　　This holy shrine, the gentle fine is this,—
　　My lips, two blushing pilgrims, ready stand
　　To smooth that rough touch with a tender kiss.

75 goodman boy: Capulet insults Tybalt by calling him names that imply he is childish and inferior in rank; **go to:** that's enough
77 God shall mend my soul: exclamation of impatience
78 mutiny: riot
79 set cock-a-hoop: upset everything

❓ **80–86** During this speech, Capulet interrupts his scolding of Tybalt with orders to the servants and comments to the guests. How would his voice and gestures change as he addresses these various parties?
81 saucy: rude
82 This kind of behavior (**trick**) may cause you trouble (**scathe you**).
84 hearts: hearties/dancers; **princox:** an overbearing, vain youngster
87–88 This forced restraint (**patience perforce**) of my anger (**choler**) makes me tremble.

❓ **89–90** What does Tybalt mean?

91–94 Romeo and Juliet now take center stage. They are instantly, deeply attracted to each other. Instead of expressing their feelings directly, they use religious metaphors. Romeo says that Juliet is like a religious shrine and compares his own lips to **pilgrims** (those who visit holy places). He says that if he has mistreated her with his rough hand, then his lips are ready to make things better with a kiss.

✱ **Shakespeare's Sonnets** The first fourteen lines that Romeo and Juliet share (lines 91–104) form a sonnet, a common style for love poetry in this era. Shakespeare wrote other sonnets around the time of *Romeo and Juliet*, but because they expressed private feelings, did not publish them. When a publisher got hold of 154 of them and printed them without permission, Shakespeare was possibly embarrassed and furious—but they are among the loveliest poems in the English language.

Juliet appears to be as entranced with Romeo as he is with her. They flirt and exchange a secret kiss.

Laurence Olivier and Vivien Leigh in a 1940
production that opened in New York.

JULIET. Good pilgrim, you do wrong your hand too much,   95
 Which mannerly devotion shows in this;
 For saints have hands that pilgrims' hands do touch,
 And palm to palm is holy palmers' kiss.

ROMEO. Have not saints lips, and holy palmers too?

JULIET. Ay, pilgrim, lips that they must use in prayer.   100

ROMEO. O, then, dear saint, let lips do what hands do;
 They pray; grant thou, lest faith turn to despair.

JULIET. Saints do not move, though grant for prayers' sake.

ROMEO. Then move not while my prayer's effect I take.
 Thus from my lips, by thine my sin is purg'd.   105

[Kissing her.]

95–98 Juliet continues the religious metaphor by replying that saints and pilgrims can put their palms together in a holy kiss. (Putting palms together represents praying; palmers were pilgrims who carried palm leaves when they visited the Holy Lands.)

❓ 99–105 Paraphrase the rest of the lines on this page.

103 saints do not . . . for prayers' sake: The saints do not voluntarily intercede in human affairs, but they may be moved to action by prayer.
105 purg'd: cleansed

❓ What is everyone else in the room doing as Romeo and Juliet speak to each other?

The Nurse appears to tell Juliet that Lady Capulet is asking for her. Juliet leaves. Romeo asks the Nurse about Juliet and learns that she is a Capulet. Benvolio comes to get Romeo so that they might leave. Lord Capulet encourages everyone to stay, until he discovers how late it is.

JULIET. Then have my lips the sin that they have took.

ROMEO. Sin from my lips? O trespass sweetly urg'd!
Give me my sin again. *[They kiss again.]*

JULIET.   You kiss by the book.

NURSE. Madam, your mother craves a word with you.

ROMEO. What is her mother?

NURSE.   Marry, bachelor,   110
Her mother is the lady of the house.
And a good lady, and a wise and virtuous:
I nurs'd her daughter that you talk'd withal;
I tell you, he that can lay hold of her
Shall have the chinks.

ROMEO.   Is she a Capulet?   115
O dear account! my life is my foe's debt.

BENVOLIO. Away, be gone; the sport is at the best.

ROMEO. Ay, so I fear; the more is my unrest.

CAPULET. Nay, gentlemen, prepare not to be gone;
We have a trifling foolish banquet towards.—   120

[They whisper in his ear.]

Is it e'en so? why then, I thank you all;
I thank you, honest gentlemen; good-night.—
More torches here!—Come on then, let's to bed.
Ah, sirrah *[to 2 Capulet]*, by my fay, it waxes late;
I'll to my rest.   125

[Exeunt all but JULIET and NURSE.]

JULIET. Come hither, nurse. What is yond gentleman?

NURSE. The son and heir of old Tiberio.

108 by the book: according to formal rules

115 shall have the chinks: shall become rich (due to her father's wealth)

❓ How does Romeo react to the news that Juliet is a Capulet?

116 dear: costly; **my life is my foe's debt:** My life belongs to my enemy.

120 towards: coming up

124 fay: faith

All leave the party except Juliet and the Nurse. Juliet asks who Romeo is and discovers he is a Montague. She is overwhelmed and dismayed by the fact that she has fallen in love with her family's enemy.

JULIET. What's he that now is going out of door?

NURSE. Marry, that, I think, be young Petruchio.

JULIET. What's he that follows there, that would not dance?   130

NURSE. I know not.

JULIET. Go ask his name: if he be marrièd,
My grave is like to be my wedding-bed.

NURSE. His name is Romeo, and a Montague;
The only son of your great enemy.   135

JULIET. My only love sprung from my only hate!
Too early seen unknown, and known too late!
Prodigious birth of love it is to me,
That I must love a loathèd enemy.

NURSE. What's this? What's this?

JULIET.   A rhyme I learn'd even now   140
Of one I danc'd withal.

[One calls within, 'Juliet.']

NURSE.   Anon, anon!
Come, let's away; the strangers all are gone.

[Exeunt.]

? Why does Juliet inquire about the identities of two other men before she asks about Romeo? How does she react when she learns that Romeo is a Montague?

138 prodigious: unlucky

PERSONA JOURNAL

If you have worked at the party, how has your evening gone? If you have been a guest, record your observations about the food, entertainment, guests, and hosts. Also, share any gossip that you've heard.

TALES FROM THE STAGE

Women were not allowed to perform on Elizabethan stages, so Shakespeare's female characters were first portrayed by teenaged males. A woman wouldn't play Juliet until 1662. Later, another kind of gender-switching was tried in Shakespeare's plays. Women played male characters, including Hamlet and Richard III. In the 1800s, Charlotte Cushman was an especially celebrated Romeo, playing opposite her sister Susan's Juliet. A newspaper printed the following review of Charlotte's performance in December 1835.

"It is enough to say that the Romeo of Miss Cushman is far superior to any Romeo we have ever had. The distinction is not one of degree, it is one of kind. For a long time Romeo has been a convention. Miss Cushman's Romeo is a creation, a living, breathing, animated, ardent human being. Miss Cushman looks Romeo exceedingly well; her deportment is frank and easy; she walks the stage with an air of command; her eye beams with animation."

Two images of the Cushman sisters in their roles as Romeo and Juliet.

61

Reacting to Act I

Analysis

1. Why do you think Shakespeare "gives away" the plot of his play in the prologue to Act I?

2. Do you believe some things are fated to happen, no matter what? Or do you believe that your actions can change the course of your life? Explain your answer.

3. What do you think might have caused the feud between the Capulets and the Montagues?

4. What does the Nurse think of Juliet and the Capulet family? What do they think of her?

5. Analyze the behavior of Tybalt, Mercutio, and Benvolio in Act I. Based on your analysis, predict what their roles might be in the rest of the play.

6. Do Romeo's feelings for Juliet seem to be different from his feelings for Rosaline? Why or why not?

7. Compare Romeo's reaction to Juliet's when each discovers the true identity of the other.

8. From what you know at this point, do you think Juliet would be better off with Paris or Romeo?

9. Using a Venn diagram, select a major character from the first act and compare your persona to that character.

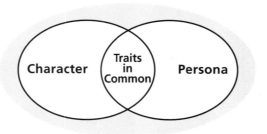

Literary Elements

1. In literary language, the term **foil** refers to a character with qualities that are in sharp contrast to another character, thus emphasizing the qualities of each. How is Mercutio a foil to Romeo?

2. **Foreshadowing** in literature refers to hints about what is to occur later in the text. What example of foreshadowing do you find in scene iv of Act I?

Writing

1. Write a description of Romeo based on what you have learned about him. Use specific quotes from the play to support your writing.

2. Assume that you write an advice column for a newspaper or magazine. A modern day Romeo (or Juliet) writes to you asking for your advice. He or she explains what happened at the party and also mentions the family feud. First write his or her letter and then write your response.

Romeo and Juliet
ACT II

John Stride and Joanna Dunham in a 1960 Franco
Zeffirelli production at London's Old Vic Theatre.

"How cam'st thou hither, tell me and wherefore?"

Romeo and Juliet have fallen in love at first sight, and Rosaline has been quickly forgotten. The CHORUS warns about the difficulties the young lovers will face because their families are enemies.

THE PROLOGUE

[Enter CHORUS.*]*

CHORUS. Now old desire doth in his deathbed lie,
　　And young affection gapes to be his heir;
That fair for which love groan'd for, and would die,
　　With tender Juliet match'd, is now not fair.
Now Romeo is belov'd, and loves again,　　　　　　　　　5
　　Alike bewitchèd by the charm of looks;
But to his foe suppos'd he must complain,
　　And she steal love's sweet bait from fearful hooks:
Being held a foe, he may not have access
　　To breathe such vows as lovers us'd to swear;　　　10
And she as much in love, her means much less
　　To meet her new belovèd anywhere:
But passion lends them power, time means, to meet,
Tempering extremities with extreme sweet.

[Exit.]

1 old desire: love for Rosaline

2 gapes: yearns

3 fair: beautiful woman (in this case Rosaline)

4 match'd: compared

6 Alike: both

7 complain: declare (his love)

14 Tempering extremities: easing extreme difficulties

❓ What obstacles does the Chorus predict Romeo and Juliet will face?

Is This Sonnet Necessary? "The use of this chorus is not easily discovered," grumbled Samuel Johnson, the 18th-century writer and critic. Johnson complained that this Act II prologue doesn't move the plot. So why did Shakespeare use a Chorus to recite a sonnet here? Perhaps it's because the sonnet makes an important point, that while Romeo is free to come and go, Juliet must generally stay indoors. This will be an obstacle for the lovers in the coming act.

Samuel Johnson

Setting the Scene

ROMEO AND JULIET

Act II, scenes i and ii *or* Pledges of Love

Critical Query: Do you think it's possible to fall in love this fast?

From the Prop Box

garlands to trim the balcony

Behind the Scene

Scene ii in this act, one of the most famous in all of Shakespeare, is known simply as the "balcony scene." It is so familiar that it is often a subject of satire or parody. Try your hand at turning romance into laughter by converting the balcony scene into a soap opera, a cartoon strip, or a Saturday Night Live skit.

Famous Quotes from Scene ii

But soft! what light through yonder window breaks? It is the east and Juliet is the sun.

O Romeo, Romeo! wherefore art thou Romeo?

What's in a name? that which we call a rose by any other name would smell as sweet.

Good night, good night! parting is such sweet sorrow.

Word Play: Imagery

Imagery refers to an author's use of words for their appeal to the senses of sight, hearing, touch, taste, and smell. Such language carries a powerful emotional impact, providing the reader or listener with vivid mental images. Romeo and Juliet overflows with images of all kinds, especially those of light and dark. Be on the lookout for them as you read scenes i and ii. (For more about imagery, see pages 10–11.)

Classroom Set Design

Set up the room with regular Capulet/Montague divided seating and an acting area at the front of the classroom. Juliet should use the teacher's desk as her "balcony." Two desks or chairs can serve as the orchard wall.

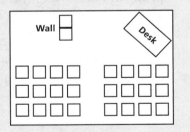

Warm-up Improv: Trust Me

You fall in love with a used car (or another item of your choice). You want the salesperson to promise not to sell it until the weekend when you say you'll return with the money. The salesperson doesn't know whether he/she can trust you or not and wants more proof of your good intentions.

Romeo leaves the party, but his love for Juliet calls him back. Unseen, he leaps over a wall into the Capulet garden. Mercutio and Benvolio look for their friend and, thinking he is still infatuated with Rosaline, call out for him with teasing comments about love.

ACT II.

Scene i. Outside Capulet's orchard

[Enter ROMEO.*]*

ROMEO. Can I go forward when my heart is here?
  Turn back, dull earth, and find thy centre out.

[He climbs the wall and leaps down within it.]

[Enter BENVOLIO *and* MERCUTIO.*]*

BENVOLIO. Romeo! my cousin Romeo!

MERCUTIO.   He is wise;
  And, on my life, hath stol'n him home to bed.

BENVOLIO. He ran this way, and leap'd this orchard wall: 5
  Call, good Mercutio.

MERCUTIO.   Nay, I'll conjure too.—
  Romeo! humours! madman! passion! lover!
  Appear thou in the likeness of a sigh:
  Speak but one rhyme, and I am satisfied;
  Cry but 'Ah me!' pronounce but 'Love' and 'dove;'   10
  Speak to my gossip Venus one fair word,
  One nickname for her purblind son and heir,
  Young Adam Cupid, he that shot so trim
✱ When King Cophetua lov'd the beggar-maid!—
  He heareth not, he stirreth not, he moveth not;   15
  The ape is dead, and I must conjure him.—

2 earth: body (Romeo); **centre:** heart (Juliet)

6 conjure: use magic or a spell to make him appear

11 gossip: confidant or close friend; **Venus:** Roman goddess of love, she is the mother of Cupid.
12 purblind: completely blind
13 Adam: believed to be a reference to Adam Bell, a famous archer in English ballads
16 The ape is dead: Romeo is compared to a trained ape that plays dead until its master gives it the command to sit up.

✱ **King Cophetua and the Beggar Maid**   According to a ballad of Shakespeare's time, King Cophetua was a king who vowed to live a chaste life. But one day, his eyes fell upon a beautiful beggar woman, and Cupid shot him with an arrow at that very moment. The king fell in love with the woman and married her. When Mercutio speaks of "he that shot so trim," he is referring to this ballad, apparently a favorite of Shakespeare's, since he used it in other plays.

Mercutio continues to tease Romeo for his lovesick behavior. He says he will lure Romeo out of his hiding place by calling up an image of Rosaline. When it becomes obvious that Romeo does not want to be found, Benvolio and Mercutio leave.

I conjure thee by Rosaline's bright eyes,
By her high forehead and her scarlet lip,
By her fine foot, straight leg, and quivering thigh,
And the demesnes that there adjacent lie,   20
That in thy likeness thou appear to us!

BENVOLIO. An if he hear thee, thou wilt anger him.

MERCUTIO. This cannot anger him: 'twould anger him
To raise a spirit in his mistress' circle,
Of some strange nature, letting it there stand   25
Till she had laid it, and conjur'd it down;
That were some spite: my invocation
Is fair and honest, and, in his mistress' name,
I conjure only but to raise up him.

BENVOLIO. Come, he hath hid himself among these trees,   30
To be consorted with the humorous night:
Blind is his love, and best befits the dark.

MERCUTIO. If love be blind, love cannot hit the mark.
Now will he sit under a medlar tree,
And wish his mistress were that kind of fruit   35
As maids call medlars when they laugh alone.—
O, Romeo, that she were, O, that she were
An open *et cetera*, thou a poperin pear!
Romeo, good night.—I'll to my truckle-bed;
This field-bed is too cold for me to sleep: 40
Come, shall we go?

BENVOLIO.   Go then; for 'tis in vain
To seek him here that means not to be found.

[Exeunt.]

17–21 Mercutio continues trying to make Romeo appear by making suggestive references about Rosaline. How will he say these lines?
20 demesnes: areas

23–29 This . . . him: If I had suggested that a stranger was with Rosaline, that would be a reason for anger (**spite**). My spell (**invocation**) only calls for Romeo.

31 consorted: familiar; **humorous:** damp

34–38 medlars: apple-like fruit. Medlars and pears were vulgar slang terms for sexual organs.

38 et cetera: This is thought to be the work of a censor who replaced the term "arse" with the Latin phrase meaning "and so forth."
40 truckle-bed: trundle bed, a low footed bed stored under a taller bed when not in use

Romeo has heard the taunting of his friends and begins to comment on their attempts to make fun of him when he suddenly sees Juliet at a window. He is overwhelmed by her beauty, comparing her to the sun, the stars, and the heavens.

Scene ii. Capulet's Orchard

[Enter ROMEO.*]*

ROMEO. He jests at scars that never felt a wound.—

✱ *[*JULIET *appears above at a window.]*

But soft! what light through yonder window breaks?
It is the east, and Juliet is the sun!—
Arise, fair sun, and kill the envious moon,
Who is already sick and pale with grief,
That thou her maid art far more fair than she: 5
Be not her maid, since she is envious;
Her vestal livery is but sick and green,
And none but fools do wear it; cast it off.—
It is my lady; O, it is my love!
O, that she knew she were!—   10
She speaks, yet she says nothing: what of that?
Her eye discourses, I will answer it.—
I am too bold, 'tis not to me she speaks:
Two of the fairest stars in all the heaven,   15
Having some business, do entreat her eyes
To twinkle in their spheres till they return.
What if her eyes were there, they in her head?
The brightness of her cheek would shame those stars,
As daylight doth a lamp; her eyes in heaven   20
Would through the airy region stream so bright
That birds would sing and think it were not night.—
See how she leans her cheek upon her hand!
O that I were a glove upon that hand,
That I might touch that cheek!

1 He jests . . . wound: He (Mercutio) makes fun of the pain of love because he has never been hurt by it.

❓ As he hears his friends calling out to him, how do you think Romeo feels about their teasing?
2 soft: wait; **breaks:** appears

8 vestal livery: virgin's clothing. (Romeo imagines that Juliet is a servant to Diana, virgin goddess of the moon.)

13 discourses: speaks

15–17 If two stars had to leave the sky, they would beg (**entreat**) Juliet's eyes to take their place.

❓ How does Romeo's description of Juliet compare to Mercutio's description of Rosaline in the previous scene?

✱ **Balcony? What Balcony?**   The "balcony scene" is the most famous scene in *Romeo and Juliet*. But did Juliet stand on a balcony in Shakespeare's original production? Note that the stage direction says that she "appears above at a window." An Elizabethan theater actually did have a balcony-like gallery directly behind and above the stage, but this was used for seating. (See theatre diagram on page 206.) Poor Juliet probably played this greatest of all love scenes at a mere window above the stage.

Juliet, believing that she is alone, reflects upon her love for Romeo. She laments the fact that he is a Montague, and wishes he had some other name.

JULIET.   Ah me!

ROMEO.   She speaks:—   25
 O, speak again, bright angel! for thou art
 As glorious to this night, being o'er my head,
 As is a wingèd messenger of heaven
 Unto the white-upturnèd wondering eyes
 Of mortals that fall back to gaze on him   30
 When he bestrides the lazy-pacing clouds
 And sails upon the bosom of the air.

✳ **JULIET.** O Romeo, Romeo! wherefore art thou Romeo?
 Deny thy father and refuse thy name;
 Or, if thou wilt not, be but sworn my love,   35
 And I'll no longer be a Capulet.

ROMEO. *[Aside.]* Shall I hear more, or shall I speak at this?

JULIET. 'Tis but thy name that is my enemy;—
 Thou art thyself, though not a Montague.
 What's Montague? It is nor hand, nor foot,   40
 Nor arm, nor face, nor any other part
 Belonging to a man. O, be some other name!
 What's in a name? that which we call a rose
 By any other name would smell as sweet;
 So Romeo would, were he not Romeo call'd,   45
 Retain that dear perfection which he owes
 Without that title:—Romeo, doff thy name;
 And for that name, which is no part of thee,
 Take all myself.

❓ Why do you think Romeo chooses images from the heavens to describe Juliet?

33–36 What does Juliet wish Romeo would do? What is she willing to do?

38–44 Juliet thinks she is alone. She tries to convince herself that a name has no importance. Someone or something is still the same no matter what name it has.

46 owes: owns
47 doff: take off or throw off
48 for: in exchange for

✳ TALES FROM THE STAGE

In 1961, the famous British actress Judi Dench was playing Juliet when she called out longingly, "O Romeo, Romeo! wherefore art thou Romeo?"
 "Down there, ducks," replied an audience member, "underneath yer balcony."
The heckler misunderstood this line, as do many others. "Wherefore" means "why," not "where." So Juliet isn't asking *where* Romeo is, but *why* his name is Montague.

John Stride and Judi Dench

Romeo calls out from below and offers to change his name if Juliet wishes it. Juliet is startled, but quickly realizes that the intruder is Romeo. She expresses concern for Romeo's safety, as it is dangerous for him to be on Capulet property.

ROMEO.   I take thee at thy word:
Call me but love, and I'll be new baptiz'd;   50
Henceforth I never will be Romeo.

JULIET. What man art thou that, thus bescreen'd in night,
So stumblest on my counsel?

ROMEO.   By a name
I know not how to tell thee who I am:
My name, dear saint, is hateful to myself,   55
Because it is an enemy to thee.
Had I it written, I would tear the word.

JULIET. My ears have yet not drunk a hundred words
Of that tongue's utterance, yet I know the sound;
Art thou not Romeo, and a Montague?   60

ROMEO. Neither, fair saint, if either thee dislike.

JULIET. How cam'st thou hither, tell me, and wherefore?
✱ The orchard walls are high and hard to climb;
And the place death, considering who thou art,
If any of my kinsmen find thee here.   65

ROMEO. With love's light wings did I o'erperch these walls;
For stony limits cannot hold love out:
And what love can do, that dares love attempt;
Therefore thy kinsmen are no stop to me.

JULIET. If they do see thee, they will murder thee.   70

52 **bescreen'd:** hidden

53 **So stumblest on my counsel?:** overhears my secret thoughts

❓ Why does Romeo not want to identify himself?

62 **hither:** here

65 **kinsmen:** relatives

66 **o'erperch:** fly over

✱ **Wall? What Wall?**   Benvolio and Juliet refer to the wall that Romeo supposedly climbs over to enter the Capulet's garden. Scholars have tried in vain to figure out what wall they mean. Because realistic scenery was seldom used on an Elizabethan stage, it seems unlikely that a wall was moved onto the stage for Romeo to jump over. Some scholars think Romeo might have entered from among the groundlings, not from backstage.

Romeo tells Juliet that he would face any danger and travel any distance to be with her. Juliet is embarassed that she has been overheard daydreaming about him, and asks Romeo if he truly loves her.

ROMEO. Alack, there lies more peril in thine eye
   Than twenty of their swords: look thou but sweet,
   And I am proof against their enmity.

JULIET. I would not for the world they saw thee here.

ROMEO. I have night's cloak to hide me from their sight;   75
   And, but thou love me, let them find me here.
   My life were better ended by their hate
   Than death proroguèd, wanting of thy love.

JULIET. By whose direction found'st thou out this place?

ROMEO. By love, that first did prompt me to enquire;   80
   He lent me counsel, and I lent him eyes.
   I am no pilot; yet, wert thou as far
   As that vast shore wash'd with the furthest sea,
   I would adventure for such merchandise.

JULIET. Thou knowest the mask of night is on my face;   85
   Else would a maiden blush bepaint my cheek
   For that which thou hast heard me speak to-night.
   Fain would I dwell on form, fain, fain deny
   What I have spoke; but farewell compliment!
   Dost thou love me, I know thou wilt say Ay;   90
   And I will take thy word: yet, if thou swear'st,
✱ Thou mayst prove false; at lovers' perjuries,
   They say Jove laughs. O gentle Romeo,
   If thou dost love, pronounce it faithfully:

73 proof: protected; **enmity:** hostility

76 And, but thou love me: if only you love me
77–78 I'd rather have my life ended by your relatives than have death delayed (**proroguèd**) and live without (**wanting of**) your love.

81 counsel: advice
82 pilot: ship captain; **wert:** were

84 adventure: travel; **merchandise:** treasure
85–89 Thou . . . compliment: It's dark, otherwise, you'd see me blushing over the things you heard me say. If I could, I'd gladly (**fain**) do the proper thing (**dwell on form**), but it's too late for formal manners (**compliment**).

92 perjuries: lies

✱ **". . . at lovers' perjuries, / They say Jove laughs."** Jove had good reason to laugh at "lovers' perjuries." The Roman king of the gods (Zeus in Greek mythology), Jove was infamous for his own romantic mischief. Although married to the goddess Juno (the Greek Hera), he had a number of extramarital affairs, including many with mortal women. Frequently, he seduced women by disguising himself in some way—as a shower of gold, a bull, or a swan.

Juliet begs Romeo not to judge her too harshly for showing her love so quickly. She says she is so overwhelmed that she has forgotten proper behavior. Romeo assures Juliet that he is sincere, and offers to swear an oath to prove it.

Or if thou thinkest I am too quickly won,   95
I'll frown, and be perverse, and say thee nay,
So thou wilt woo: but else, not for the world.
In truth, fair Montague, I am too fond;
And therefore thou mayst think my 'haviour light:
But trust me, gentleman, I'll prove more true   100
Than those that have more cunning to be strange.
I should have been more strange, I must confess,
But that thou overheard'st, ere I was 'ware,
My true-love passion: therefore pardon me;
And not impute this yielding to light love,   105
Which the dark night hath so discoverèd.

ROMEO. Lady, by yonder blessèd moon I swear,
That tips with silver all these fruit-tree tops,—

JULIET. O, swear not by the moon, the inconstant moon,
That monthly changes in her circled orb,   110
Lest that thy love prove likewise variable.

ROMEO. What shall I swear by?

JULIET.   Do not swear at all;
Or if thou wilt, swear by thy gracious self,
Which is the god of my idolatry,
And I'll believe thee.

ROMEO.   If my heart's dear love,—   115

JULIET. Well, do not swear: although I joy in thee,
I have no joy of this contract to-night;

85–106 Plot out this long speech of Juliet's. Where will she change her tone, her mood, her rate of speech?

95–104 If you think I've fallen in love too quickly, I'll pretend it's not really true (**say thee nay**), and then you can court (**woo**) me. I know I'm acting foolish (**fond**) and so you may think I'm immodest (**light**), but trust me. You'll find me more faithful than those who have a greater ability to act shy (**strange**) and play games. Really, I would have acted more properly, but I wasn't aware that you were listening to my passionate words.

105 impute: attribute

Why doesn't Juliet want Romeo to swear by the moon?

Does Juliet feel vulnerable? How do you know?

114 of my idolatry: that I worship

117 contract: pledge (of love)

Shakespeare Goes to Oxford   According to legend, a leather-bound first edition of Shakespeare's collected plays (published in 1623) was added to a library at Oxford University, attached to a chain so it could not be removed. Only a few pages of the huge book were worn through from reading and re-reading by Oxford students. They were the pages of this love scene between Romeo and Juliet, and their farewell in Act III, scene v.

Juliet worries that things are happening too fast. Romeo wants to exchange vows of love before he goes. Suddenly the Nurse calls, and Juliet ducks inside, promising to return to the window shortly.

It is too rash, too unadvis'd, too sudden;
Too like the lightning, which doth cease to be
Ere one can say "it lightens." Sweet, good night!   120
This bud of love, by summer's ripening breath,
May prove a beauteous flower when next we meet.
Good night, good night! As sweet repose and rest
Come to thy heart as that within my breast!

ROMEO. O, wilt thou leave me so unsatisfied?   125

JULIET. What satisfaction canst thou have to-night?

ROMEO. The exchange of thy love's faithful vow for mine.

JULIET. I gave thee mine before thou didst request it;
And yet I would it were to give again.

ROMEO. Would'st thou withdraw it? For what purpose, love?   130

JULIET. But to be frank and give it thee again.
And yet I wish but for the thing I have;
My bounty is as boundless as the sea,
My love as deep; the more I give to thee,
The more I have, for both are infinite.   135
I hear some noise within: dear love, adieu!—

[NURSE calls within.]

Anon, good nurse!—Sweet Montague, be true.
Stay but a little, I will come again.

[Exit.]

ROMEO. O blessèd, blessèd night! I am afeard,
Being in night, all this is but a dream,   140
Too flattering-sweet to be substantial.

? 126 What might Juliet really be asking Romeo about "satisfaction"?

133 bounty: generosity; **boundless:** endless

139 afeard: afraid

141 substantial: real

PERSONA JOURNAL

Tell about your first true love. Compare and contrast your experience with that of Romeo and Juliet.

Juliet returns and asks Romeo to prove his sincerity by arranging for their marriage the next day. The Nurse again calls Juliet to come inside. Romeo, elated by Juliet's love, begins to leave when she calls him back once more.

[Enter JULIET above.]

JULIET. Three words, dear Romeo, and good night indeed.
   If that thy bent of love be honourable,
   Thy purpose marriage, send me word to-morrow,
   By one that I'll procure to come to thee,   145
   Where and what time thou wilt perform the rite;
   And all my fortunes at thy foot I'll lay
   And follow thee, my lord, throughout the world.

NURSE. *[Within.]* Madam!

JULIET. I come anon.— But if thou meanest not well,   150
   I do beseech thee,—

NURSE. *[Within.]* Madam!

JULIET.   By-and-by I come:—
   To cease thy suit and leave me to my grief:
   To-morrow will I send.

ROMEO. So thrive my soul,—   155

JULIET. A thousand times good night! *[Exit.]*

ROMEO. A thousand times the worse, to want thy light!—
   Love goes toward love as schoolboys from their books;
   But love from love, towards school with heavy looks.

[Retiring slowly.]

[Re-enter JULIET, above.]

✱ **JULIET.** Hist! Romeo, hist!—O for a falconer's voice   160
   To lure this tassel-gentle back again!
   Bondage is hoarse and may not speak aloud;

143 bent: intention

145 procure: arrange
146 rite: ceremony

❓ Do you think Romeo minds that Juliet wants to get married the very next day?

151 beseech: beg

152 By-and-by: at once
153 cease thy suit: stop pursuing me

155 So thrive my soul: Romeo swears by his soul that his love is true.

158–159 Love . . . looks: Lovers join each other with the same joy that schoolboys have when they put away their books. Lovers part from each other with a sadness like boys headed off to class.

161 tassel-gentle: a male falcon
162 Bondage is hoarse . . . aloud: I am bound by my father's rules and must not be overheard.

✱ **"O for a falconer's voice . . ."** Falconry is an ancient sport, dating perhaps to the 8th century B.C. It reached the peak of its popularity in England during Shakespeare's time, and there are several references to it throughout his plays. Around the time *Romeo and Juliet* was written, there were many rules and laws concerning falconry, especially what kinds of birds could be used by people of different social ranks.

Juliet asks for details about the next day's arrangements. The two exchange banter, not wanting to part but knowing that they should.

Else would I tear the cave where Echo lies,
And make her airy tongue more hoarse than mine
With repetition of my Romeo's name.   165

ROMEO. It is my soul that calls upon my name:
How silver-sweet sound lovers' tongues by night,
Like softest music to attending ears!

JULIET. Romeo!

ROMEO.   My dear?

JULIET.   At what o'clock
Tomorrow shall I send to thee?

ROMEO.   At the hour of nine.   170

JULIET. I will not fail: 'tis twenty years till then.
I have forgot why I did call thee back.

ROMEO. Let me stand here till thou remember it.

JULIET. I shall forget, to have thee still stand there,
Remembering how I love thy company.   175

ROMEO. And I'll still stay, to have thee still forget,
Forgetting any other home but this.

JULIET. 'Tis almost morning; I would have thee gone:
✱ And yet no farther than a wanton's bird;
That lets it hop a little from her hand,   180
Like a poor prisoner in his twisted gyves,
And with a silk thread plucks it back again,
So loving-jealous of his liberty.

ROMEO. I would I were thy bird.

---

163 Echo: a maiden in Greek mythology who could only repeat what others said

169 My dear: Yes, my sweet?

174 still: always

179 wanton's bird: a spoiled child's pet

181 gyves: chains on the legs of prisoners

❓ Who seems more sensible and mature—Romeo or Juliet? Why?

✱ **Conceits**   Juliet says that she wants to let Romeo go away "no farther than a wanton's bird." For the next six lines, she and Romeo continue this comparison, imagining Romeo as a pet bird belonging to Juliet. This kind of extended comparison is called a *conceit*. Conceits were extremely common in love poetry of Shakespeare's time, and you will find many more of them in *Romeo and Juliet*.

At last, the couple says goodnight. Since it is nearly morning, Romeo sets off for Friar Lawrence's to tell him what has happened and to ask for his help.

JULIET.   Sweet, so would I:
   Yet I should kill thee with much cherishing.   185
   Good night, good night! parting is such sweet sorrow
   That I shall say good night till it be morrow.

[Exit.]

ROMEO. Sleep dwell upon thine eyes, peace in thy breast!—
   Would I were sleep and peace, so sweet to rest!
   Hence will I to my ghostly father's cell,   190
   His help to crave and my dear hap to tell.

[Exit.]

190 ghostly father's cell: spiritual father's (priest's) room
191 His help to . . . tell: To ask for (**crave**) his help and to tell him of my good fortune (**dear hap**).

PERSONA JOURNAL

What would you do or say if you knew that Romeo and Juliet were planning a secret wedding?

Leslie Howard and Norma Shearer in a 1936
film of *Romeo and Juliet* directed by George Cukor.

Setting the Scene
ROMEO AND JULIET
Act II, scene iii *or* True Confessions

Critical Query: What are the positives and negatives of the Friar's involvement with Romeo and Juliet's wedding?

Time Capsule

People have always used plants and herbs as medicine. During the Renaissance, herbalists paid close attention to the shapes and colors of plants. A leaf shaped like the human liver was thought to be good for the liver. A mandrake root, shaped like a man, was thought to be good for the whole body. The marigold's yellow flower was thought to be good for healing jaundice, which made the skin yellow. And like Friar Lawrence in the following scene, Renaissance herbalists believed that plants had much to teach about human nature.

From the Prop Box

basket and scissors for the Friar

In Character: The Friendly Friar

The Friar will be extremely important to the development of the plot. See what you can learn about him as you read scene iii.

Warm-up Improv: Pretty Please

A friend asks you for a big favor which he/she knows you might be reluctant to grant. For example:

- Your friend wants to borrow your car. (He put a dent in it the last time he used it.)
- Your friend wants to borrow your new leather jacket. (When she borrowed your best shirt she spilled pizza down the front of it.)

- Your friend wants to swap schedules with you at work. (The last time you agreed to this he didn't show up at the right time.)

Talk this through with your friend and then decide whether you will agree to the request or not.

Friar Lawrence is tending his herb garden. As he works, he considers the various medicinal uses of the plants.

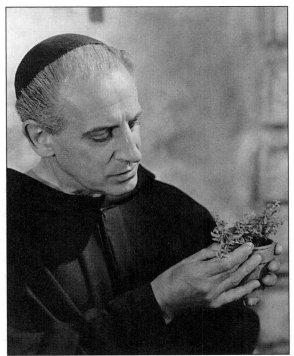

Max Adrian as Friar Lawrence. Stratford-upon-Avon, 1961

Scene iii. Friar Lawrence's Cell

[Enter FRIAR LAWRENCE with a basket.]

FRIAR. The grey-ey'd morn smiles on the frowning night,
    Chequering the eastern clouds with streaks of light;
    And fleckèd darkness like a drunkard reels
    From forth day's path and Titan's fiery wheels:
    Now, ere the sun advance his burning eye,   5
    The day to cheer and night's dank dew to dry,
    I must up-fill this osier cage of ours
    With baleful weeds and precious-juicèd flowers.
    The earth, that's nature's mother, is her tomb;
    What is her burying grave, that is her womb: 10
    And from her womb children of divers kind
    We sucking on her natural bosom find;
    Many for many virtues excellent,
    None but for some, and yet all different.
    O, mickle is the powerful grace that lies   15
    In plants, herbs, stones, and their true qualities:

2 Chequering: dappling

4 Titan's fiery wheels: In Greek mythology, the sun god drove his wheeled chariot across the sky each day.

7 osier cage: a wicker basket

8 baleful: poisonous; **precious-juiced:** healing

9–13 Mother earth's womb holds the buried dead and also gives birth to many (**divers**) kinds of useful plants.

PERSONA JOURNAL

Like everyone else in Verona, you know Friar Lawrence. Describe him.

15 mickle: great; **grace:** goodness

Friar Lawrence continues to ponder the good and evil uses of the herbs, and compares them to human nature. Romeo arrives, alarming the Friar, who assumes Romeo must be very troubled to visit at such an early hour.

Foreshadow

Everything has a little good & evil

For naught so vile that on the earth doth live
But to the earth some special good doth give;
Nor aught so good but, strain'd from that fair use,
Revolts from true birth, stumbling on abuse: 20
Virtue itself turns vice, being misapplied;
And vice sometimes by action dignified.
Within the infant rind of this small flower
Poison hath residence, and medicine power:
For this, being smelt, with that part cheers each part;   25
Being tasted, slays all senses with the heart.
Two such opposèd kings encamp them still
In man as well as herbs,—grace and rude will;
And where the worser is predominant,
Full soon the canker death eats up that plant.   30

[Enter ROMEO.*]*

ROMEO. Good morrow, father!

FRIAR.   *Benedicite!*
What early tongue so sweet saluteth me?—
Young son, it argues a distemper'd head
So soon to bid good morrow to thy bed:
Care keeps his watch in every old man's eye,   35

17–20 There is nothing (**naught**) so evil that it doesn't have some good in it, nor anything (**aught**) so good that it can't be dangerous when misused.

 Do you agree with the Friar that there is some good or usefulness in everything?

25 for . . . part: it benefits every part of the body
26 with the heart: and stops the heart
28 grace and rude will: good and evil

30 canker: a reference to the cankerworm which eats and destroys plants

31 *Benedicite!:* God bless you!
32 saluteth: greets
33 distemper'd head: troubled mind

Richard Burbage

Shakespeare Acts Up As an actor, Shakespeare is said to have had a fine voice, making him strong in dignified roles—kings, ghosts, honest old servants, and such. But he was not a leading man and surely did not play Romeo. That role probably went to his favorite actor, Richard Burbage. Some scholars think Shakespeare may have played Friar Lawrence when *Romeo and Juliet* was first performed, and that he later took on the role of the Chorus.

At first the Friar guesses that Romeo has spent the night with Rosaline. Romeo assures him that this is not the case and tells of his love for Juliet. He asks the Friar to marry them that very day.

And where care lodges sleep will never lie;
But where unbruisèd youth with unstuff'd brain
Doth couch his limbs, there golden sleep doth reign:
Therefore thy earliness doth me assure
Thou art uprous'd with some distemperature;   40
Or if not so, then here I hit it right,—
Our Romeo hath not been in bed to-night.

ROMEO. That last is true; the sweeter rest was mine.

FRIAR. God pardon sin! Wast thou with Rosaline?

ROMEO. With Rosaline, my ghostly father? no;   45
I have forgot that name, and that name's woe.

FRIAR. That's my good son: but where hast thou been then?

ROMEO. I'll tell thee ere thou ask it me again.
I have been feasting with mine enemy;
Where, on a sudden, one hath wounded me   50
That's by me wounded. Both our remedies
Within thy help and holy physic lies;
I bear no hatred, blessèd man; for, lo,
My intercession likewise steads my foe.

FRIAR. Be plain, good son, and homely in thy drift;   55
Riddling confession finds but riddling shrift.

ROMEO. Then plainly know my heart's dear love is set
On the fair daughter of rich Capulet:
As mine on hers, so hers is set on mine;
And all combin'd, save what thou must combine   60
By holy marriage: when, and where, and how
We met, we woo'd, and made exchange of vow,
I'll tell thee as we pass; but this I pray,
That thou consent to marry us to-day.

36 lodges: stays

37 unbruised: innocent;
unstuff'd: untroubled

38 couch: rest

40 Thou art . . . distemperature:
You are upset (**uprous'd**) over
some problem (**distemperature**).

? 44 What does the Friar think
might have happened?

PERSONA JOURNAL

What kind of relationship do you
have with the Friar? Do you confide
in him as well?

52 physic: medicine (Romeo is
referring to the marriage ceremony.)

54 My . . . foe: My request (**intercession**) also benefits (**steads**) my
enemy.
55 homely in thy drift: speak
clearly and to the point
56 riddling: unclear, confused;
shrift: absolution (forgiveness of
sins)

60 combin'd: agreed

Shakespeare's Catholicism   During the 1530s, King Henry VIII broke from the Roman Catholic Church
and became head of the Church of England. By the time of Shakespeare's birth in 1564, it had become
dangerous to practice Catholicism in England. Nevertheless, many of today's scholars believe that
Shakespeare was secretly raised a Catholic. If so, his religious background surely contributed to his
sympathetic portrayal of Friar Lawrence.

Friar Lawrence can't believe what he is hearing! Could Romeo be in love with Rosaline one day and Juliet the next? He claims that Romeo still has salt stains on his cheek from the tears wept over Rosaline. Romeo reminds the Friar that he himself advised Romeo to forget Rosaline. Besides, as Romeo points out, Rosaline did not return his love, while Juliet does.

FRIAR. Holy Saint Francis! what a change is here!   65
✱ Is Rosaline, that thou didst love so dear,
So soon forsaken? young men's love, then, lies
Not truly in their hearts, but in their eyes.
Jesu Maria, what a deal of brine
Hath wash'd thy sallow cheeks for Rosaline!   70
How much salt water thrown away in waste,
To season love, that of it doth not taste!
The sun not yet thy sighs from heaven clears,
Thy old groans ring yet in mine ancient ears;
Lo, here upon thy cheek the stain doth sit   75
Of an old tear that is not wash'd off yet:
If e'er thou wast thyself, and these woes thine,
Thou and these woes were all for Rosaline;
And art thou chang'd? Pronounce this sentence then,—
Women may fall, when there's no strength in men.   80

ROMEO. Thou chidd'st me oft for loving Rosaline.

FRIAR. For doting, not for loving, pupil mine.

ROMEO. And bad'st me bury love.

FRIAR.   Not in a grave
To lay one in, another out to have.

ROMEO. I pray thee chide not: she whom I love now   85
Doth grace for grace and love for love allow;
The other did not so.

69 Jesu Maria, what a deal of brine: Son of Mary, what a lot of tears
70 sallow: pale

❓ Why does the Friar not believe Romeo?

Rosaline too quick

79 Pronounce this sentence: say this proverb

81 chidd'st me oft: scolded me often
82 doting: infatuation

✱ **Where is Rosaline?** In his 1968 film version of *Romeo and Juliet*, director Franco Zeffirelli cut every single reference to Rosaline before this scene. Zeffirelli seemed to feel that Romeo's love sickness for Rosaline was a distraction from the main story. Do you think *Romeo and Juliet* would have been a better, tighter play if Shakespeare had left out Rosaline altogether? Or does Romeo's early, shallow infatuation highlight the depth of his love for Juliet?

Friar Lawrence agrees to marry Romeo and Juliet in hopes that the marriage will end the feud between families. At the same time, he cautions Romeo against haste.

FRIAR.   O, she knew well
    Thy love did read by rote, that could not spell.
    But come, young waverer, come go with me,
    In one respect I'll thy assistant be;   90
    For this alliance may so happy prove,
    To turn your households' rancour to pure love.

ROMEO. O, let us hence; I stand on sudden haste.

✱ **FRIAR.** Wisely, and slow; they stumble that run fast.

    [Exeunt.]

88 read by rote, that could not spell: repeat words that you memorized
89 waverer: changeable young man

92 rancour: bitterness

93 stand: insist

❓ If the Friar has agreed to an immediate marriage, why do you think he cautions Romeo against moving too quickly?

✱ **"Wisely, and slow; they stumble that run fast."**   This saying of the Friar's comes from a Latin phrase *festina lente*, which means "hasten slowly." The Friar believes strongly in the ancient idea of the "golden mean," which held that people should practice "moderation in all things," avoiding extremes of any kind. He will express this idea elsewhere in the play—but he will find it hard to persuade Romeo to follow it.

Setting the Scene
ROMEO AND JULIET
Act II, scene iv *or* Our Hero, Happy at Last

Critical Query: In what ways has Romeo changed since the play began?

Behind the Scene: Persona Alert

Personas should divide into three groups. Numbering off 1,2,3 is an easy way to accomplish this. As scene iv opens, Group One personas should be standing around the edges of the acting area as part of a street crowd. They should react to what is said and done by the main characters. Notice that Group Two replaces Group One when the Nurse and Peter enter on page 88. Group Three gets its turn on page 90 when Benvolio and Mercutio exit.

Word Play: Pun-ishment and Prose

1. Get set for a pun free-for-all! Mercutio, Benvolio, and Romeo engage in a furious battle of wits in this scene. Who do you think will win this war of words?
2. Is this scene written mainly in prose or poetry? Why do you think it was written this way? Who speaks in verse? Who speaks in poetry? Who switches back and forth? For more about prose and poetry, see pages 9–10.

From the Prop Box

- Fan for the Nurse
- Apron for the Nurse
- Sword for Mercutio (plastic or foam)
- Coins for Romeo

In Character: The Nurse

You'll learn a lot more about the Nurse in this scene. What do you think people say about her behind her back?

Warm-up Improv: Secret Message

Two friends are teasing you relentlessly about the person you dated last Friday. They don't stop until your date's older sister appears. Your friends leave, and the sister, who is a bit scatterbrained, gives you a lecture about treating her younger sister/brother right. She finally remembers that she was supposed to deliver a note to you (from your date, of course!).

Mercutio and Benvolio know that Tybalt has sent a letter to Romeo's house, and they suspect that he has challenged Romeo to a fight. The two friends worry that Romeo, in his present lovesick condition, is no match for the swordsmanship of Tybalt.

Scene iv. A Street

[Enter BENVOLIO *and* MERCUTIO.*]*

MERCUTIO. Where the devil should this Romeo be?—
Came he not home to-night?

BENVOLIO. Not to his father's; I spoke with his man.

MERCUTIO. Ah, that same pale hard-hearted wench, that Rosaline,
Torments him so that he will sure run mad.   5

BENVOLIO. Tybalt, the kinsman to old Capulet,
Hath sent a letter to his father's house.

MERCUTIO. A challenge, on my life.

BENVOLIO. Romeo will answer it.

MERCUTIO. Any man that can write may answer a letter.   10

BENVOLIO. Nay, he will answer the letters master, how he dares,
being dared.

MERCUTIO. Alas, poor Romeo, he is already dead! stabbed with a
white wench's black eye; shot through the ear with a love
song; the very pin of his heart cleft with the blind bow-boy's   15
butt-shaft: and is he a man to encounter Tybalt?

BENVOLIO. Why, what is Tybalt?

MERCUTIO. More than prince of cats, I can tell you. O, he's the
courageous captain of compliments. He fights as you sing
prick-song—keeps time, distance, and proportion; rests me   20
his minim rest, one, two, and the third in your bosom: the
very butcher of a silk button, a duellist, a duellist; a
gentleman of the very first house,—of the first and second
✱ cause: ah, the immortal *passado*! the *punto reverso*! the *hay*.—

PERSONA ACTION

Group One is "on the street," reacting to the conversation among Romeo, Mercutio, and Benvolio.

2 to-night: last night

3 man: servant

8 challenge: challenge to a duel; **on my life:** I'll bet my life on it.
9 Romeo will answer it: He will agree to fight.

❓ Why would Tybalt want to fight with Romeo?

15–16 the very pin . . . shaft: The very center (**pin**) of his heart split (**cleft**) with Cupid's practice arrow (**blind boy's butt-shaft**).

18 prince of cats: A play on Tybalt's name, Tybert was the name of the Prince of Cats in the fable" Reynard the Fox."
19–20 captain of compliments: model of foppish or overly-fashionable behavior; **as you sing prick-song:** as you would sing from a piece of music
21 minim rest: short pause in music
23 very first house: best fencing school

✱ **"Ah, the immortal *passado*! the *punto reverso*! the *hay*."**   Unlike his Queen Mab speech, Mercutio's rantings about swordplay are anything but fantasy; they are quite authentic. The "passado" is an attack which combines a sword thrust with foot movements. The "punto reverso" is a back-handed thrust. And the "hay" is a thrust that strikes one's opponent. Mercutio clearly knows his swordsmanship.

As Mercutio and Benvolio continue to discuss Tybalt, Romeo appears. Their relentless teasing begins again as they mockingly compare Rosaline to the famous beauties of history.

BENVOLIO. The what?   25

MERCUTIO. The pox of such antic, lisping, affecting fantasticoes; these new tuners of accents!—By Jesu, a very good blade!—a very tall man! –a very good whore!'—Why, is not this a lamentable thing, grandsire, that we should be thus afflicted with these strange flies, these fashion-mongers, these *perdona-mi's*, who stand so much on the new form that they cannot sit at ease on the old bench? O, their bones, their bones!   30

[Enter ROMEO.]

BENVOLIO. Here comes Romeo, here comes Romeo!

MERCUTIO. Without his roe, like a dried herring.—O flesh, flesh,   35
how art thou fishified!—Now is he for the numbers that
✷ Petrarch flowed in: Laura, to his lady, was but a kitchen wench,—marry, she had a better love to be-rhyme her; Dido, a dowdy; Cleopatra, a gypsy; Helen and Hero, hildings and harlots; Thisbe, a gray eye or so, but not to the purpose,—   40
[Enter ROMEO.] Signior Romeo, *bon jour*! There's a French salutation to your French slop. You gave us the counterfeit fairly last night.

ROMEO. Good morrow to you both. What counterfeit did I give you?   45

MERCUTIO. The slip, sir, the slip; can you not conceive?

ROMEO. Pardon, good Mercutio, my business was great; and in such a case as mine a man may strain courtesy.

MERCUTIO. That's as much as to say, such a case as yours constrains a man to bow in the hams.   50

ROMEO. Meaning, to court'sy.

MERCUTIO. Thou hast most kindly hit it.

---

26 pox: plague; **antic:** grotesque; **fantasticoes:** snobs
27 new tuners of accents: those who use words that are in the latest fashion
28 tall: brave
29 lamentable: terrible, regrettable; **grandsire:** old man (kiddingly to Benvolio)
30 flies: parasites
31 *perdona-mi*: "pardon me" in Italian; **form:** <u>dual meaning</u> bench or fashion
32 bones: a pun on the French word *bon* (**good**)
❷ Mercutio comments sarcastically about Tybalt's overdone manners and flashy swordsmanship. What tone of voice and type of gestures might he use?
35 roe: <u>dual meaning</u> fish eggs or a female deer. (Mercutio's elaborate pun plays on Romeo's name. RO-meo without the "roe" implies that he is gutless and/or without a female partner.)
36–37 numbers: verses; **Petrarch:** writer of love sonnets to Laura
39 hildings: worthless creatures
42 French slop: French style pants; **counterfeit:** <u>dual meaning</u> slip (giving someone the slip) or fake money
46 conceive: understand
48 courtesy: <u>dual meaning</u> manners or a bow

50 hams: legs

52 hit it: <u>dual meaning</u> get the point or sexual intercourse

---

✷ **Femme Fatales** The Italian poet Petrarch (1304–1374) addressed his sonnets of chaste love to Laura. Four of the other heroines mentioned here committed suicide for love—Dido, queen of Carthage, after being jilted by the hero Aeneas; Cleopatra, queen of Egypt, after the death of the Roman hero Antony; Hero after the death of her lover Leander; and Thisbe after the death of her lover Pyramus. Helen was so beautiful that the Trojan War was fought over her.

Mercutio and Romeo engage in a furious round of jokes and puns based on words such as *courtesy, pink, pump, sole,* and *goose*.

ROMEO. A most courteous exposition.

MERCUTIO. Nay, I am the very pink of courtesy.

ROMEO. Pink for flower.   55

MERCUTIO. Right.

ROMEO. Why, then is my pump well-flowered.

MERCUTIO. Well said: follow me this jest now till thou hast worn out thy pump; that, when the single sole of it is worn, the jest may remain, after the wearing, sole singular.   60

ROMEO. O single-soled jest, solely singular for the singleness!

MERCUTIO. Come between us, good Benvolio; my wits faint.

ROMEO. Switch and spurs, switch and spurs; or I'll cry a match.

MERCUTIO. Nay, if thy wits run the wild-goose chase, I have done; for thou hast more of the wild-goose in one of thy wits than, I   65
am sure, I have in my whole five: was I with you there for the goose?

ROMEO. Thou wast never with me for anything when thou wast not there for the goose.

MERCUTIO. I will bite thee by the ear for that jest.   70

ROMEO. Nay, good goose, bite not.

MERCUTIO. Thy wit is a very bitter sweeting; it is a most sharp sauce.

ROMEO. And is it not, then, well served in to a sweet goose?

✳ **MERCUTIO.** O, here's a wit of cheveril, that stretches from an inch   75
narrow to an ell broad!

ROMEO. I stretch it out for that word 'broad:' which added to the goose, proves thee far and wide a broad goose.

❓ Find as many double and triple meanings as you can in the speeches on this page.

57 pump: shoe; **well-flowered:** decorated with punched patterns

60 sole singular: <u>dual meaning</u> weak or unique
61 single-soled jest, solely singular for the singleness: what a weak joke, unique only because it's so pathetic
63 Switch . . . match: Keep your wits moving at full gallop or I'll claim victory in this game of words.
64 wild-goose chase: a game of follow-the-leader on horseback. The goal was to catch the goose.
66–67 was I with you there for the goose: Didn't I hit home at the end of the game?
69 goose: prostitute

72 sweeting: type of sweet apple

74 a sweet goose: refers to Mercutio

76 ell broad: 45 inches wide

78 broad goose: pun meaning "indecent"

✳ **Butcher's Boy or Glover's Son?**   According to folklore, young William Shakespeare was a Stratford "butcher's boy" who made grand speeches when slaughtering calves. Actually, Shakespeare's father, John, was a glovemaker—although he might have done some butchering on the side. Mercutio makes a reference to the glover's trade when he speaks of a "wit of cheveril." Cheveril is highly stretchable, flexible leather from a kid (young goat).

As the jokes continue, Romeo sees the Nurse and her servant Peter coming towards them.

MERCUTIO. Why, is not this better now than groaning for love?
  now art thou sociable, now art thou Romeo; now art thou   80
  what thou art, by art as well as by nature: for this drivelling
  love is like a great natural, that runs lolling up and down to
  hide his bauble in a hole.

BENVOLIO. Stop there, stop there.

MERCUTIO. Thou desirest me to stop in my tale against the hair.   85

BENVOLIO. Thou wouldst else have made thy tale large.

MERCUTIO. O, thou art deceived; I would have made it short: for
  I was come to the whole depth of my tale; and meant indeed
  to occupy the argument no longer.

ROMEO. Here's goodly gear!   90

[Enter NURSE *and* PETER.*]*

  A sail, a sail, a sail!

MERCUTIO. Two, two; a shirt and a smock.

NURSE. Peter!

PETER. Anon.

NURSE. My fan, Peter.   95

MERCUTIO. Good Peter, to hide her face; for
  her fan's the fairer face.

NURSE. God ye good morrow, gentlemen.

MERCUTIO. God ye good-den, fair gentlewoman.

NURSE. Is it good-den?   100

81 drivelling: silly

82 natural: fool

83 bauble: <u>dual meaning</u> Jester's pole or male sex organ

85 stop in my tale against the hair: stop telling my story when I don't want to. Tale also refers to the male sex organ.

86 large: indecent

90 goodly gear: good stuff to joke about

PERSONA ACTION

As the Nurse and Peter enter, Group Two replaces Group One as street observers.

91 A sail: Apparently, the Nurse looks like a huge ship moving down the street.

92 a shirt and a smock: a man and a woman (the Nurse and her attendant, Peter)

98 God ye good morrow: God give you good morning

99 God ye good-den: God give you good afternoon

100 Is it good-den: Is it afternoon already?

TALES FROM THE STAGE

The role of Peter was first played by a famous comedian named William Kempe. Kempe was notorious for making up his own dialogue. Some scholars believe that he and Shakespeare quarreled over this issue and parted ways. Shakespeare was probably thinking of Kempe when his character Hamlet grumbled to a troupe of players, "And let those that play your clowns speak no more than is set down for them . . ."

Engraving of William Kempe (right), 1600

Mercutio begins to tease the Nurse with bawdy jokes. The Nurse asks where Romeo is. Romeo identifies himself. Mercutio and Benvolio leave after agreeing to meet later at Romeo's house.

MERCUTIO. 'Tis no less, I tell ye; for the bawdy hand of the dial is now upon the prick of noon.

NURSE. Out upon you! what a man are you!

ROMEO. One, gentlewoman, that God hath made for himself to mar.　　　105

NURSE. By my troth, it is well said;—'or himself to mar,' quoth 'a?—Gentlemen, can any of you tell me where I may find the young Romeo?

ROMEO. I can tell you: but young Romeo will be older when you have found him than he was when you sought him: I am the　110 youngest of that name, for fault of a worse.

NURSE. You say well.

MERCUTIO. Yea, is the worst well? very well took, i' faith; wisely, wisely.

✳ NURSE. If you be he, sir, I desire some confidence with you.　　115

BENVOLIO. She will indite him to some supper.

MERCUTIO. A bawd, a bawd, a bawd! So ho!

ROMEO. What hast thou found?

MERCUTIO. No hare, sir; unless a hare, sir, in a lenten pie, that is something stale and hoar ere it be spent. *[Sings.]*　　120

　　An old hare hoar,
　　And an old hare hoar,
　　　　Is very good meat in Lent;
　　But a hare that is hoar
　　Is too much for a score　　125
　　　　When it hoars ere it be spent.

Romeo, will you come to your father's? We'll to dinner thither.

101–102 'Tis no less, I . . . noon: a sexual joke to shock the Nurse

104–105 that God hath . . . mar: who was made to harm himself

106 By my troth: truly

111 fault: lack

113 well took: perceptive

117 bawd: owner of a house of prostitution; **So ho!:** I found her!

119 hare: prostitute; **hare:** rabbit; **lenten pie:** Lent is a religious period of forty days preceding Easter, when many Christians do not eat meat. If a lenten pie contained hare, it would get stale and moldy (**hoar**), since it would not be eaten.
120 something: somewhat; **hoar ere:** old before
121–126 The song lyrics contain many puns on the words *hair/hare* and *whore/hoar*. *Hoar* can also mean gray.

128 thither: there

✳ **Malapropisms** When the Nurse says "confidence" when she means "conference," she is making a comical mistake called a malapropism. The word comes from Mrs. Malaprop, a character in an 18th-century play. Notice that Benvolio mocks the Nurse by responding with another malapropism—"indite" instead of "invite."

The Nurse complains to Romeo that she has been abused by his friends. She scolds Peter for not defending her honor.

ROMEO. I will follow you.

MERCUTIO. Farewell, ancient lady; farewell,—[*singing*] lady, lady, 130
lady.

[*Exeunt* MERCUTIO, *and* BENVOLIO.]

NURSE. Marry, farewell!—I pray you, sir, what saucy merchant was
this that was so full of his ropery?

ROMEO. A gentleman, nurse, that loves to hear himself talk; and
will speak more in a minute than he will stand to in a month. 135

NURSE. An 'a speak anything against me, I'll take him down, an
'a were lustier than he is, and twenty such Jacks; and if I
cannot, I'll find those that shall. Scurvy knave! I am none of
his flirt-gills; I am none of his skains-mates.—And thou must
stand by too, and suffer every knave to use me at his pleasure! 140

PETER. I saw no man use you at his pleasure; if I had, my weapon
should quickly have been out, I warrant you: I dare draw as
soon as another man, if I see occasion in a good quarrel, and
the law on my side.

The Nurse takes her anger out
on the unfortunate Peter.
(Zeffirelli, 1968)

? Do you think the Nurse enjoys
Mercutio's teasing? Why or why
not?

130–131 lady, lady, lady: most
likely a line from a popular ballad

PERSONA ACTION

As Mercutio and Benvolio exit,
Group Three replaces Group Two
"on the street."

132 saucy merchant: indecent fellow

133 ropery: The Nurse means
"roguery"(vulgar ways).

135 stand to: stand to listen to

136–137 an 'a were lustier: even if
he were bigger; **Jacks:** rascals

138–139 Scurvy knave: disgusting
troublemaker; **flirt-gills:** loose
women; **skains-mates:** gangsters

142 warrant: guarantee

The Nurse warns Romeo not to mistreat Juliet. Romeo explains the wedding arrangements. Juliet is to pretend to go to Friar Lawrence's for confession where, instead, she'll be married. At that time, the Nurse will wait outside, where Romeo's servant will give her a rope ladder that Juliet can drop down for him later that night.

NURSE. Now, afore God, I am so vexed that every part about me 145
    quivers. Scurvy knave!—Pray you, sir, a word: and, as I told
    you, my young lady bid me enquire you out; what she bade
    me say I will keep to myself: but first let me tell ye, if ye
    should lead her into a fool's paradise, as they say, it were a
    very gross kind of behaviour, as they say: for the gentlewoman 150
    is young; and, therefore, if you should deal double with her,
    truly it were an ill thing to be offered to any gentlewoman,
    and very weak dealing.

ROMEO. Nurse, commend me to thy lady and mistress. I protest
    unto thee,— 155

NURSE. Good heart, and i' faith I will tell her as much: Lord,
    Lord, she will be a joyful woman.

ROMEO. What wilt thou tell her, nurse? thou dost not mark me.

NURSE. I will tell her, sir,—that you do protest: which, as I take it,
    is a gentlemanlike offer. 160

ROMEO. Bid her devise
    some means to come to shrift this afternoon;
    And there she shall at Friar Lawrence' cell
    Be shriv'd and married. Here is for thy pains.

NURSE. No, truly, sir; not a penny. 165

ROMEO. Go to; I say you shall.

NURSE. This afternoon, sir? well, she shall be there.

ROMEO. And stay, good nurse, behind the abbey-wall:
    Within this hour my man shall be with thee,
    And bring thee cords made like a tackled stair; 170
    Which to the high top-gallant of my joy
    Must be my convoy in the secret night.
    Farewell; be trusty, and I'll quit thy pains:
    Farewell; commend me to thy mistress.

145 vexed: annoyed

Is the Nurse really upset or just pretending to be so?

What warning does the Nurse give Romeo? Why does she do this?

154 commend me: "pay my respects" or "give my love"

158 mark: listen to

162 shrift: confession

164 shriv'd: absolved

164 Romeo tries to give the Nurse some money for her help. Do you think she wants it? Does she take it? Why or why not?
166 Go to: not another word

170 bring thee cords . . . stair: will bring you a rope ladder
171 top-gallant: highest point
172 convoy: passageway
173 quit thy pains: reward you

The Nurse rattles on and on about Juliet and the wedding plans until Romeo finally sends her on her way.

NURSE. Now God in heaven bless thee!—Hark you, sir. 175

ROMEO. What say'st thou, my dear nurse?

NURSE. Is your man secret? Did you ne'er hear say,
Two may keep counsel, putting one away?

ROMEO. I warrant thee, my man's as true as steel.

NURSE. Well, sir; my mistress is the sweetest lady.—Lord, Lord! 180
when 'twas a little prating thing,—O, there's a nobleman in
town, one Paris, that would fain lay knife aboard; but she,
good soul, had as lief see a toad, a very toad, as see him. I
anger her sometimes, and tell her that Paris is the properer
man; but I'll warrant you, when I say so, she looks as pale as 185
any clout in the versal world. Doth not rosemary and Romeo
begin both with a letter?

ROMEO. Ay, nurse; what of that? both with an *R*.

NURSE. Ah, mocker! that's the dog's name. *R* is for the dog: no; I
know it begins with some other letter:—and she hath the 190
prettiest sententious of it, of you and rosemary, that it would
do you good to hear it.

ROMEO. Commend me to thy lady.

NURSE. Ay, a thousand times. *[Exit ROMEO.]* Peter!

PETER. Anon? 195

NURSE. Peter, take my fan, and go before and apace. 196

[Exeunt.]

175 **hark you:** listen

177 **secret:** trustworthy
178 **Two may keep . . . away:** Two can keep a secret if one is dead.

181 **prating:** chattering foolishly
182 **would fain lay knife aboard:** eagerly take for himself whatever he wants
183 **lief:** willingly; **a very:** an actual
184 **properer:** more handsome
186 **clout in the versal world:** rag in the universe

189 **mocker:** teaser; **that's the dog's name:** because it sounds like a dog growling—r-r-r-r
191 **sententious:** another of the Nurse's malapropisms. She means "sentences."

196 **apace:** quickly

PERSONA JOURNAL

You've seen the Nurse and Peter around the town. Describe them.

Setting the Scene
ROMEO AND JULIET
Act II, scene v *or* No News Is Bad News

Critical Query: What might explain the Nurse's behavior in this scene?

Classroom Set Design

Standard Montague/Capulet divided seating with two chairs or a bench upstage left for Juliet and the Nurse to sit on. Note that in theatrical terms, *upstage* means away from the audience and *downstage* means toward or closer to the audience. Left and right refer to the actor's left and right sides as he or she faces the audience.

| Bench |
Upstage Left

From the Prop Box

- Fan for the Nurse
- Apron for the Nurse

In Character: Hypochondria?

In scene v, the Nurse complains about her health instead of giving Juliet news from Romeo. As you read or listen to this scene, list all the aches and pains she claims to have. Do you think she is really ill?

Warm-up Improv: Spill the Beans

You are dying to know what your parents are getting you for your sixteenth birthday. Your little brother or sister knows but he/she's not telling. Use every trick you can think of to pry the information out of him/her.

Juliet waits in the Capulet orchard, anxious for the Nurse's return. Finally, the Nurse and Peter arrive.

Scene v. Capulet's Orchard

[Enter JULIET.]

✱ **JULIET.** The clock struck nine when I did send the nurse;
In half an hour she promis'd to return.
Perchance she cannot meet him: that's not so.—
O, she is lame! love's heralds should be thoughts,
Which ten times faster glide than the sun's beams,   5
Driving back shadows over lowering hills:
Therefore do nimble-pinion'd doves draw love,
And therefore hath the wind-swift Cupid wings.
Now is the sun upon the highmost hill
Of this day's journey; and from nine till twelve   10
Is three long hours,—yet she is not come.
Had she affections and warm youthful blood,
She'd be as swift in motion as a ball;
My words would bandy her to my sweet love,
And his to me: 15
But old folks, many feign as they were dead;
Unwieldy, slow, heavy and pale as lead.—
O God, she comes!

[Enter NURSE and PETER].

                          O honey nurse, what news?
Hast thou met with him? Send thy man away.

NURSE. Peter, stay at the gate.   20

[Exit PETER.]

JULIET. Now, good sweet nurse,—O Lord, why look'st thou sad?

> ❓ As Juliet waits nervously for news from Romeo, what thoughts might be going through her head? Would she move around the stage, or stay in one place?

3 Perchance: perhaps

4 heralds: messengers

6 lowering: darkening

7 nimble-pinion'd doves draw love: fast-winged doves pull Venus' chariot

14 bandy: toss

16 feign as: appear as if

✱ **Time Lapse?** "The clock struck nine when I did send the nurse," says Juliet. But we know that the Nurse didn't meet Romeo until noon. (See page 89, lines 101–102.) Did Shakespeare make a mistake in his time scheme? Or did he want us to wonder what the Nurse was doing during those three morning hours?

Juliet is eager for news from Romeo, but the Nurse complains about her health and mutters to herself about other unrelated matters. Juliet tries to be patient, but her frustration soon shows.

Though news be sad, yet tell them merrily;
If good, thou sham'st the music of sweet news
By playing it to me with so sour a face.

NURSE. I am aweary, give me leave awhile;—   25
Fie, how my bones ache! what a jaunce have I had!

JULIET. I would thou hadst my bones, and I thy news:
Nay, come, I pray thee speak;—good, good nurse, speak.

NURSE. Jesu, what haste? can you not stay awhile?
Do you not see that I am out of breath?   30

JULIET. How art thou out of breath, when thou hast breath
To say to me that thou art out of breath?
The excuse that thou dost make in this delay
Is longer than the tale thou dost excuse.
Is thy news good or bad? answer to that;   35
Say either, and I'll stay the circumstance:
Let me be satisfied, is't good or bad?

NURSE. Well, you have made a simple choice; you know not how
to choose a man: Romeo! no, not he. Though his face be
better than any man's, yet his leg excels all men's; and for a   40
hand and a foot, and a body,—though they be not to be
talked on, yet they are past compare: he is not the flower of
courtesy,—but I'll warrant him as gentle as a lamb.—Go thy
ways, wench; serve God. What, have you dined at home?

JULIET. No, no: but all this did I know before.   45
What says he of our marriage? what of that?

NURSE. Lord, how my head aches! what a head have I!
It beats as it would fall in twenty pieces.
My back o' t' other side,—O, my back, my back!—

23 sham'st: misuse

25 give me leave: let me rest
26 Fie: an expression of disgust or dismay; jaunce: rough journey

36 stay the circumstance: wait for the details
37 be satisfied: know
38 simple: foolish

What does the Nurse really think of Romeo? How do you know?

Claire Bloom as Juliet and Athene Seyler as the Nurse
(Old Vic, 1952)

Beshrew your heart for sending me about   50
To catch my death with jauncing up and down!

JULIET. I' faith, I am sorry that thou art not well.
Sweet, sweet, sweet nurse, tell me, what says my love?

NURSE. Your love says, like an honest gentleman, and a
courteous, and a kind, and a handsome; and, I warrant, a   55
virtuous,—Where is your mother?

50 Beshrew your heart: Shame on you
51 jauncing: bouncing

As Juliet reaches the limit of her patience, the Nurse finally relates the news of the wedding plans, including details about the rope ladder that Romeo will use to reach Juliet's room. Blushing and excited, Juliet leaves for Friar Lawrence's cell.

JULIET. Where is my mother?—why, she is within;
Where should she be? How oddly thou repliest!
'Your love says, like an honest gentleman,—
" 'Where is your mother?' "

NURSE.   O God's Lady dear!   60
Are you so hot? Marry, come up, I trow;
Is this the poultice for my aching bones?
Hence forward, do your messages yourself.

JULIET. Here's such a coil!—come, what says Romeo?

NURSE. Have you got leave to go to shrift to-day?   65

JULIET. I have.

NURSE. Then hie you hence to Friar Lawrence' cell;
There stays a husband to make you a wife:
Now comes the wanton blood up in your cheeks,
They'll be in scarlet straight at any news.   70
Hie you to church; I must another way,
To fetch a ladder, by the which your love
Must climb a bird's nest soon when it is dark:
I am the drudge, and toil in your delight;
But you shall bear the burden soon at night.   75
Go; I'll to dinner; hie you to the cell.

JULIET. Hie to high fortune!—honest nurse, farewell.

[Exeunt.]

61 Are you . . . trow: Are you so impatient? Really, come now, I declare.
62 poultice: a warm medicated cloth
63 hence forward: from now on

64 coil: fuss

67 hie you hence: hurry

69 wanton: passionate
70 in scarlet: blushing

74 drudge: worker

Setting the Scene
ROMEO AND JULIET
Act II, scene vi *or* Tying the Knot

Critical Query: What are the possible consequences of Romeo and Juliet's marriage?

From the Prop Box

Head covering for Juliet

Classroom Set Design

Use the same design as scene v, but move the bench downstage left to serve as an altar.

Downstage Left

Altar

Word Play: Imagery and Foreshadowing

This scene, as Romeo and Juliet prepare to marry, should be filled with joy and light. But notice how many images of death and violence are on these two pages. Jot down as many of these images as you can. What do they foreshadow about the future?

Time Capsule: Wedding Traditions

What sort of marriage vows did Romeo and Juliet exchange? Although Renaissance marriages varied greatly, the lovers might have said something like this:

ROMEO: I, Romeo, give my body to you, Juliet, in loyal matrimony.

JULIET: And I receive it. And I, Juliet, give my body to you, Romeo, in loyal matrimony.

ROMEO: And I receive it.

Then Romeo was supposed to slip a ring on Juliet's finger.

Warm-up Improv: Rock On!

You and a partner are parents of a teen who wants to skip college and tour with a rock band. You know you can't stop your child | from touring, but you have many misgivings that you want to express.

Romeo shares his feelings for Juliet with the Friar. Nevertheless, the Friar expresses reservations about the marriage and warns of excess passion. Juliet arrives.

Scene vi. Friar Lawrence's Cell

[Enter FRIAR LAWRENCE *and* ROMEO.*]*

FRIAR. So smile the heavens upon this holy act
    That after-hours with sorrow chide us not!

ROMEO. Amen, amen! but come what sorrow can,
    It cannot countervail the exchange of joy
    That one short minute gives me in her sight: 5
    Do thou but close our hands with holy words,
    Then love-devouring death do what he dare,—
    It is enough I may but call her mine.

FRIAR. These violent delights have violent ends,
    And in their triumph die; like fire and powder,   10
    Which, as they kiss, consume: the sweetest honey
    Is loathsome in his own deliciousness,
    And in the taste confounds the appetite:
    Therefore love moderately: long love doth so;
    Too swift arrives as tardy as too slow.   15

[Enter JULIET.*]*

    Here comes the lady:—O, so light a foot
    Will ne'er wear out the everlasting flint:
    A lover may bestride the gossamer
    That idles in the wanton summer air
    And yet not fall; so light is vanity.   20

JULIET. Good-even to my ghostly confessor.

FRIAR. Romeo shall thank thee, daughter, for us both.

*[*ROMEO *kisses* JULIET.*]*

JULIET. As much to him, else is his thanks too much.

*[*JULIET *returns his kiss.]*

1–2 May heaven bless this ceremony so that we will not face sorrow or blame later (**after-hours**).

4 countervail: equal

10 powder: gunpowder

12 Is loathsome in his own deliciousness: is sickening if eaten to excess
13 confounds: destroys

Why do you think the Friar continues to advise moderation?

17 Will ne'er . . . flint: will never wear out the cobblestone path
18 bestride the gossamer: ride upon a cobweb
19 wanton: carefree
20 vanity: empty love

23 As much: the same

Romeo expresses his love to Juliet and she to him. The Friar suggests they begin the marriage ceremony.

Act II   Scene vi

If you were the Friar, would you marry Romeo and Juliet?

✶ **ROMEO.** Ah, Juliet, if the measure of thy joy
    Be heap'd like mine, and that thy skill be more   25
    To blazon it, then sweeten with thy breath
    This neighbour air, and let rich music's tongue
    Unfold the imagin'd happiness that both
    Receive in either by this dear encounter.

25 that: if

26 blazon: proclaim

27 neighbor: surrounding

JULIET. Conceit, more rich in matter than in words,   30
    Brags of his substance, not of ornament:
    They are but beggars that can count their worth;
    But my true love is grown to such excess,
    I cannot sum up sum of half my wealth.

30 Conceit: true understanding

FRIAR. Come, come with me, and we will make short work;   35
    For, by your leaves, you shall not stay alone
    Till holy church incorporate two in one.

[Exeunt.]

✶ **". . . if the measure of thy joy / Be heap'd like mine . . ."** Here, Romeo calls upon Juliet to express their love, if "thy skill be more / To blazon it . . ." And in a five-line reply, Juliet does, indeed, express this love with greater beauty and power than Romeo possibly could. Almost until the moments before his death, Romeo remains a step or two behind Juliet in maturity, depth of feeling, and self-expression.

The wedding of Romeo and Juliet as envisioned by two film directors. Above, a modern interpretation with Leonardo DiCaprio and Claire Danes (1996). Right, the Zeffirelli film (1968). Which do you prefer?

Reacting to Act II

Analysis

1. Why is Juliet embarrassed by the fact that Romeo has overheard her daydreams about him?

2. After exchanging vows of love in scene ii, Juliet says, "I have no joy of this contract to-night." What do you think she means by this?

3. Describe how Romeo and his friends treat the Nurse. Would they treat all women of Verona in the same fashion? Explain.

4. Why do you think Shakespeare left the wedding ceremony out of the play?

5. Romeo and Juliet meet each other and are married in less than twenty-four hours. Why do you think they were so anxious to marry?

6. Instead of marrying so quickly, what do you think might have happened if Romeo and Juliet had told their parents of their love and asked for their understanding?

7. Do you approve of the Nurse and the Friar's actions in helping with the secret wedding? Why or why not?

8. Use a web like the one below to map the possible consequences (both good and bad) of Romeo and Juliet's marriage.

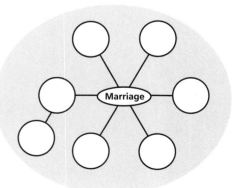

Literary Elements

1. **Dramatic Irony** is the quality present when the audience knows something that the characters on stage do not. Review the Friar's speeches at the end of scene iii and find an example of this element.

2. In drama, a **soliloquy** is a longer speech that reveals the innermost thoughts and feelings of the character who speaks it— just as if the character were speaking to himself or herself. Usually, the character is alone on the stage. If other characters are present, they do not "hear" the speech. Find soliloquies by Romeo, Juliet, and Friar Lawrence in Act II. What purpose do they serve?

3. **Imagery** refers to words that appeal to the five senses. *Romeo and Juliet* is filled with this kind of language, which adds emotion and power to the writing. To see how imagery is embedded into the play, find and list the images of light, dark, and fire in scene ii.

Writing

1. Write a character description of Friar Lawrence. What kind of person is he? Use quotations from the play to support your ideas.

2. At the beginning of scene iv, Benvolio mentions a letter that Tybalt has written to Romeo. Compose your version of this letter, using the language of Shakespeare.

3. Summarize the action of the play so far. Use one sentence for Act I and one sentence for Act II.

Romeo and Juliet

Act III

The Death of Mercutio,
Edwin Austin Abbey, 1903

"I am hurt.
A plague o'
both your
houses!"

Setting the Scene

ROMEO AND JULIET
Act III, scene i *or* Fight or Flight?

Critical Query: How does the mood of the play change during this scene?

Vocabulary: Fighting Words

alla stoccata	a fencing thrust
bandying	fighting
martial	warlike
passado	a fencing thrust with one foot forward
point	a sword
rapier	two-edged sword with narrow pointed blade

From the Prop Box

4 swords or fencing foils

Special Effects: Stage Fights

This action-filled scene requires extra preparation for those involved in the sword fights that occur. Detailed choreography and practice are necessary for combat scenes to be effective and safe.

- Actors should decide what type of fight is best suited for this scene—a violent brawl, a by-the-books fencing duel, or something in between.
- Plan each part of the fight scene step-by-step and move-by-move.
- Write down the movements for reference as you prepare.
- Rehearse the movements in slow motion. Remember to practice falls as well as fighting. It may be easier to divide the fight into segments, practicing each segment until all parties are confident of their moves.
- Most important, as you plan and rehearse, rule one is safety. No one should be hurt in a stage fight.

Classroom Set Design

This scene can best be played in the round, with chairs and personas situated on all four sides of the room. This will leave a large open space for swordplay and for personas to gather. Leave at least two openings for characters entering and exiting the square.

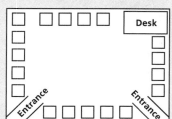

Plan the Fight Scene

In lieu of an improvisation for this scene, time should be spent with the class assisting in the planning and practice of the sword fights.

Time Capsule: The Prince Rules

At the end of this scene, Prince Escalus will have some tough decisions to make. It wasn't easy to rule a quarrelsome city like Verona during the Renaissance. Italian leaders of that time often asked themselves which was better—to be feared or loved? In his book *The Prince*, the political thinker Niccolò Machiavelli (1469–1527) said that it was *safer* to be more feared than loved. But a prince, he said, must be careful never to be hated.

Benvolio suggests that he and Mercutio return home in order to avoid the Capulets, who are roaming the streets looking for a fight. Mercutio scoffs and accuses Benvolio of having just as quick a temper as anyone else.

ACT III.

Scene i. A Public Place

[Enter MERCUTIO, BENVOLIO, PAGE, *and* SERVANTS.*]*

BENVOLIO. I pray thee, good Mercutio, let's retire:
The day is hot, the Capulets abroad,
And, if we meet, we shall not scape a brawl;
For now, these hot days, is the mad blood stirring.

MERCUTIO. Thou art like one of these fellows that, when he   5
enters the confines of a tavern, claps me his sword upon the
table, and says 'God send me no need of thee!' and by the
operation of the second cup draws him on the drawer, when
indeed there is no need.

BENVOLIO. Am I like such a fellow?   10

* **MERCUTIO.** Come, come, thou art as hot a Jack in thy mood as
any in Italy; and as soon moved to be moody, and as soon
moody to be moved.

BENVOLIO. And what to?

MERCUTIO. Nay, an there were two such, we should have none   15
shortly, for one would kill the other. Thou! why, thou wilt
quarrel with a man that hath a hair more or a hair less in his
beard than thou hast. Thou wilt quarrel with a man for
cracking nuts, having no other reason but because thou hast
hazel eyes;—what eye but such an eye would spy out such a   20
quarrel? Thy head is as full of quarrels as an egg is full of

2 abroad: out and about

3 scape: escape

4 mad blood stirring: makes tempers flare

7–8 by the operation . . . drawer: after he has felt the effects of his second drink (**cup**), he draws his weapon on the waiter (**drawer**), the one who "draws" the drink from its container.

11–13 Thou art . . . moved: You are as hot-tempered a person (**Jack**) as anyone else in Italy, and as easily provoked (**moved**) to become angry (**moody**) and when angry, as easily provoked.

14 And what to: provoked to do what?

15 two: Mercutio puns on Benvolio's "to"

* **Hot Under the Collar?**   That Mercutio "loves to hear himself talk" is plenty obvious here, and poor Benvolio is the butt of his jokes. Benvolio only wants to get indoors and away from danger—and for this, Mercutio accuses him of being quarrelsome. Mercutio is never more fanciful than in calling the easygoing Benvolio a hothead. It is Mercutio himself who is itching for a fight—and he'll soon find it.

As Mercutio's teasing of Benvolio continues, a number of Capulets arrive with Tybalt in the lead. Tybalt asks if Mercutio has seen Romeo. His choice of words sets Mercutio off on one of his characteristic word-taunting games.

meat; and yet thy head hath been beaten as addle as an egg for quarrelling. Thou hast quarrelled with a man for coughing in the street, because he hath wakened thy dog that hath lain asleep in the sun. Didst thou not fall out with a tailor for wearing his new doublet before Easter? With another for tying his new shoes with an old riband? and yet thou wilt tutor me from quarrelling!   25

BENVOLIO. An I were so apt to quarrel as thou art, any man should buy the fee simple of my life for an hour and a quarter.   30

MERCUTIO. The fee simple! O simple!

BENVOLIO. By my head, here come the Capulets.

MERCUTIO. By my heel, I care not.

[Enter TYBALT and others.]

TYBALT. Follow me close, for I will speak to them.—   35
Gentlemen, good-den: a word with one of you.

MERCUTIO. And but one word with one of us? Couple it with something; make it a word and a blow.

TYBALT. You shall find me apt enough to that, sir, an you will give me occasion.   40

MERCUTIO. Could you not take some occasion without giving?

TYBALT. Mercutio, thou consortest with Romeo,—

MERCUTIO. Consort! what, dost thou make us minstrels? An thou make minstrels of us, look to hear nothing but discords: here's my fiddlestick; here's that shall make you dance.   45
Zounds, consort!

---

22 addle: rotten

26 doublet: close fitting jacket
27 riband: lace or ribbon
28 tutor me from quarrelling: teach me how to avoid a fight
29–31 If I was as likely to quarrel as you are, any man could buy ownership (**fee-simple**) of my life for a fraction of what it's worth (**an hour and a quarter**).

? What is likely to happen now that Tybalt has arrived?

42 consortest: are friends with (usually refers to a small group of musicians)
43–44 Mercutio deliberately misinterprets Tybalt's use of the word "consort" and pretends that he and Romeo have been insulted by being called "minstrels" or wandering musicians.
45 fiddlestick: violin bow, but in this case, sword
46 Zounds: an oath literally meaning "God's wounds"

Benvolio, remembering the Prince's warning against public fighting, urges everyone to move to a more private place. Just then, Romeo arrives, and Tybalt begins a quarrel. Romeo refuses to be drawn into a fight with Tybalt, who is unaware that Romeo has just married Juliet, Tybalt's cousin.

BENVOLIO. We talk here in the public haunt of men:
Either withdraw unto some private place,
And reason coldly of your grievances,
Or else depart; here all eyes gaze on us.   50

MERCUTIO. Men's eyes were made to look, and let them gaze;
✱ I will not budge for no man's pleasure, I.

TYBALT. Well, peace be with you, sir.—Here comes my man.

[Enter ROMEO.*]*

MERCUTIO. But I'll be hanged, sir, if he wear your livery:
Marry, go before to field, he'll be your follower;   55
Your worship in that sense may call him man.

TYBALT. Romeo, the love I bear thee can afford
No better term than this,—Thou art a villain.

ROMEO. Tybalt, the reason that I have to love thee
Doth much excuse the appertaining rage   60
To such a greeting. Villain am I none;
Therefore farewell; I see thou know'st me not.

TYBALT. Boy, this shall not excuse the injuries
That thou hast done me; therefore turn and draw.

ROMEO. I do protest I never injur'd thee;   65
But love thee better than thou canst devise
Till thou shalt know the reason of my love:
And so good Capulet,—which name I tender
As dearly as mine own,—be satisfied.

❓ Why does Mercutio challenge Tybalt?

53 man: Tybalt means "the man I am seeking," but Mercutio continues to misinterpret his comments and pretends Tybalt means "man" in the sense of "servant."

54–55 There's no way he will ever wear your servant's uniform (**livery**), but just go to the dueling field and you'll see how quickly he will follow you.

58 a villain: of low birth

60 appertaining rage: the anger that would be a suitable (**appertaining**) response to such a disrespectful greeting

66 devise: imagine

❓ **66:** What does Romeo mean by this statement?
68 tender: cherish

PERSONA JOURNAL

Which of the four young men—Tybalt, Mercutio, Benvolio, Romeo—do you admire most? Explain.

✱ **Double Negatives**   Today, we are taught not to use double negatives. According to our rules, Mercutio really should say that he would "not budge for any man's pleasure." But in Shakespeare's time, double negatives were considered perfectly proper, as they are in some other languages (Spanish, for example) today.

Mercutio is outraged that Romeo will not fight, and takes it upon himself to uphold the Montague honor. Tybalt and Mercutio draw their weapons. Romeo calls to Benvolio to help him stop the fight.

MERCUTIO. O calm, dishonourable, vile submission!   70
    Alla stoccata carries it away. *[Draws.]*
    Tybalt, you rat-catcher, will you walk?

TYBALT. What wouldst thou have with me?

MERCUTIO. Good king of cats, nothing but one of your nine lives;
    that I mean to make bold withal, and, as you shall use me   75
    hereafter, dry-beat the rest of the eight. Will you pluck your
    sword out of his pilcher by the ears? make haste, lest mine be
    about your ears ere it be out.

TYBALT. I am for you. *[Drawing.]*

ROMEO. Gentle Mercutio, put thy rapier up.   80

MERCUTIO. Come, sir, your *passado.*

[They fight.]

ROMEO. Draw, Benvolio; beat down their weapons.—
    Gentlemen, for shame! forbear this outrage!—
    Tybalt,—Mercutio,—the prince expressly hath

71 *Alla stoccata:* a fencing thrust. Mercutio implies that Tybalt's fancy swordsmanship has frightened Romeo and turned Romeo into a coward.
72 rat-catcher: refers back to "Prince of Cats"; **will you walk:** will you fight with me?

? Mercutio feels that he needs to stand up for his friend, Romeo, who is being dishonored. Is he right or wrong in doing so?
75–76 make bold withal: take; **as you shall use me hereafter:** depending on how you treat me; **dry-beat the rest of the eight:** I might just give your other eight lives a sound beating instead of killing them.
77 pilcher: scabbard; **ears:** hilt
79 I am for you: I'm ready to fight you
80 rapier up: sword away
83 forbear: stop

The fight scene as staged at the Old Vic (Zeffirelli, 1960)

In an attempt to break things up, Romeo gets in between Tybalt and Mercutio. Tybalt, however, thrusts his sword underneath Romeo's arm, mortally wounding Mercutio. Tybalt leaves quickly, and Mercutio, who realizes the seriousness of his injury, curses both the Montagues and the Capulets.

    Forbid this bandying in Verona streets.—   85
    Hold, Tybalt!—good Mercutio!—

85 bandying: fighting

[TYBALT under ROMEO's arm thrusts MERCUTIO in.]

[Exeunt TYBALT with his FOLLOWERS.]

PERSONA ACTION

Demonstrate for a friend exactly how Mercutio was killed.

MERCUTIO. I am hurt;—
    A plague o' both your houses!—I am sped.—
    Is he gone, and hath nothing?

88 sped: finished

BENVOLIO.   What, art thou hurt?

89 and hath nothing?: and has no wound?

MERCUTIO. Ay, ay, a scratch, a scratch; marry, 'tis enough.—   90
    Where is my page?—go, villain, fetch a surgeon.

[Exit PAGE.]

ROMEO. Courage, man; the hurt cannot be much.

MERCUTIO. No, 'tis not so deep as a well, nor so wide as a church
    door; but 'tis enough, 'twill serve: ask for me to-morrow, and
    you shall find me a grave man. I am peppered, I warrant, for   95
    this world.—A plague o' both your houses!—Zounds, a dog, a
    rat, a mouse, a cat, to scratch a man to death! a braggart, a
    rogue, a villain, that fights by the book of arithmetic!—Why
    the devil came you between us? I was hurt under your arm.

95 a grave man: Even in death, Mercutio plays with the double meaning of words. He uses *grave*, to mean serious, as well as meaning ready for the grave; **peppered:** beaten decisively
98 by the book of arithmetic: according to the rules of fencing

ROMEO. I thought all for the best.   100

MERCUTIO. Help me into some house, Benvolio,
    Or I shall faint.—A plague o' both your houses!
    They have made worms' meat of me:
    I have it, and soundly too.—Your houses!

102 a plague o': a curse on
103 made worms' meat of me: made a corpse of me

❓ Why does Mercutio curse both houses?

[Exit MERCUTIO and BENVOLIO.]

Did Mercutio Have to Die?   According to legend, Shakespeare once remarked that he had to kill Mercutio—or Mercutio would have killed him. Mercutio doesn't seem to have been the last example of Shakespeare losing control over a character. In Shakespeare's two-part play *Henry IV*, a comical fat knight named Sir John Falstaff stole the show, winding up with more lines than the title character. Shakespeare took care to kill him off in the sequel, *Henry V*.

Romeo, upset by the injury to his friend, criticizes himself for refusing to fight. Benvolio enters to tell Romeo that Mercutio is dead. Tybalt returns and is challenged by a now enraged Romeo.

ROMEO. This gentleman, the prince's near ally,   105
My very friend, hath got his mortal hurt
In my behalf; my reputation stain'd
With Tybalt's slander,—Tybalt, that an hour
Hath been my kinsman.—O sweet Juliet,
Thy beauty hath made me effeminate   110
And in my temper soften'd valour's steel.

[Re-enter BENVOLIO.*]*

BENVOLIO. O Romeo, Romeo, brave Mercutio's dead!
That gallant spirit hath aspir'd the clouds,
Which too untimely here did scorn the earth.

ROMEO. This day's black fate on more days doth depend;   115
This but begins the woe others must end.

[Re-enter TYBALT.*]*

BENVOLIO. Here comes the furious Tybalt back again.

ROMEO. Alive in triumph! and Mercutio slain!
Away to heaven respective lenity,
And fire-ey'd fury be my conduct now!—   120
Now, Tybalt, take the 'villain' back again
That late thou gavest me; for Mercutio's soul

105 ally: relative
106 very: true

111 soften'd valour's steel: made me a coward

112 brave: noble
113 aspir'd: risen to

115 more days doth depend: casts a shadow on the days ahead

118 Alive in triumph: Tybalt celebrates his victory
119–120 Away . . . lenity: The considerate mercy (**respective lenity**) I showed before can fly away to heaven. (Romeo will no longer make excuses for Tybalt just because he's Juliet's relative.) Fiery anger will be my guide (**conduct**) now.

Laurence Olivier as Mercutio

TALES FROM THE STAGE

In 1935, the great Shakespearean actor Laurence Olivier undertook the role of Mercutio for the first time. He asked his friend Ralph Richardson, who had already played Mercutio, for advice. Once Mercutio died, Richardson explained, it was crucial for the actor playing him not to get too drunk during the hour and 25 minutes that remained before his curtain call. It wouldn't do to fall off the stage!

Romeo attacks Tybalt and kills him, thus avenging his cousin Mercutio's death. Benvolio urges Romeo to flee, as he fears the Prince will order Romeo's death for breaking the peace. Romeo leaves just before the Prince, the Montagues, the Capulets, and other townspeople gather. Benvolio begins to explain what has happened.

Is but a little way above our heads,
Staying for thine to keep him company.
Either thou or I, or both, must go with him.   125

TYBALT. Thou, wretched boy, that didst consort him here,
Shalt with him hence.

ROMEO.   This shall determine that.

[They fight; TYBALT *falls.]*

BENVOLIO. Romeo, away, be gone!
The citizens are up, and Tybalt slain.—
Stand not amaz'd. The prince will doom thee death   130
If thou art taken. Hence, be gone, away!

ROMEO. O, I am fortune's fool!

BENVOLIO.   Why dost thou stay?

[Exit ROMEO.*]*

[Enter CITIZENS, *as* OFFICERS OF THE WATCH*]*

1 CITIZEN. Which way ran he that kill'd Mercutio?
Tybalt, that murderer, which way ran he?

BENVOLIO. There lies that Tybalt.

1 CITIZEN.   Up, sir, go with me;   135
I charge thee in the prince's name obey.

[Enter PRINCE, MONTAGUE, CAPULET, *their* WIVES, *and others.]*

PRINCE. Where are the vile beginners of this fray?

BENVOLIO. O noble prince, I can discover all
The unlucky manage of this fatal brawl:
There lies the man, slain by young Romeo,   140
That slew thy kinsman, brave Mercutio.

PERSONA JOURNAL

Assume that you witnessed these two deaths. Record your reactions.

127 Shalt . . . hence: You'll be with him (in heaven) soon.

❓ Why does Romeo fight Tybalt?

130 amaz'd: in shock; **doom:** sentence

132 fortune's fool: a victim of fate

PERSONA ACTION

Everyone enters the square to hear what has happened. Remember to remain in character.

138–139 I can reveal (**discover all**) the unfortunate circumstances (**unlucky manage**) of this fatal fight

Lady Capulet demands revenge for the death of Tybalt. At the Prince's command, Benvolio continues to give the details of the recent events.

LADY CAPULET. Tybalt, my cousin! O my brother's child!—
O prince!—O husband!—O, the blood is spill'd
Of my dear kinsman!—Prince, as thou art true,
For blood of ours shed blood of Montague.—   145
O cousin, cousin!

PRINCE. Benvolio, who began this bloody fray?

BENVOLIO. Tybalt, here slain, whom Romeo's hand did slay;
Romeo, that spoke him fair, bid him bethink
How nice the quarrel was, and urg'd withal   150
Your high displeasure.—All this,—uttered
With gentle breath, calm look, knees humbly bow'd,—
Could not take truce with the unruly spleen
Of Tybalt, deaf to peace, but that he tilts
With piercing steel at bold Mercutio's breast;   155
Who, all as hot, turns deadly point to point,
And, with a martial scorn, with one hand beats
Cold death aside, and with the other sends
It back to Tybalt, whose dexterity
Retorts it: Romeo he cries aloud,   160
'Hold, friends! friends, part!' and swifter than his tongue,
His agile arm beats down their fatal points,
And 'twixt them rushes; underneath whose arm
An envious thrust from Tybalt hit the life
Of stout Mercutio, and then Tybalt fled: 165
But by-and-by comes back to Romeo,
Who had but newly entertain'd revenge,
And to't they go like lightning; for, ere I
Could draw to part them was stout Tybalt slain;
And as he fell did Romeo turn and fly.   170
This is the truth, or let Benvolio die.

(?) 148–171 Plot out this speech line by line as if you were the actor. What gestures would you use and where would you use them? What would your emotions be? Would they change as you tell this story?

149 bid him bethink: urged him to consider

150 nice: trivial

153–154 take truce with the unruly spleen of Tybalt: make peace with the hot temper of Tybalt

156 all as hot, turns deadly point to point: just as angry, turned his sword to meet Tybalt's sword

157 martial: warlike

160 Retorts: returns

162 points: sword points

164 envious: hateful

165 stout: brave

167 entertain'd: thought of

PERSONA ACTION

Remember to react appropriately as you listen to what the main characters say.

Lady Capulet accuses Benvolio of lying, and asks the Prince to put Romeo to death.

Lady Capulet grieves for Tybalt. (Zeffirelli, 1968)

LADY CAPULET. He is a kinsman to the Montague,
    Affection makes him false, he speaks not true:
    Some twenty of them fought in this black strife,
    And all those twenty could but kill one life.   175
    I beg for justice, which thou, prince, must give;
    Romeo slew Tybalt, Romeo must not live.

173 affection: bias

Why does Lady Capulet say that it must have taken twenty men to kill Tybalt?

Lord Montague defends his son as the Prince ponders what to do. He is personally affected by the tragedy since two of his kinsman, Tybalt and Mercutio, died in the fray. The Prince decides on exile rather than death for Romeo, but warns that he will be killed should he ever return to Verona.

PRINCE. Romeo slew him; he slew Mercutio:
    Who now the price of his dear blood doth owe?

MONTAGUE. Not Romeo, prince; he was Mercutio's friend;   180
    His fault concludes but what the law should end,
    The life of Tybalt.

PRINCE.   And for that offence
    Immediately we do exile him hence:
    I have an interest in your hate's proceeding,
    My blood for your rude brawls doth lie a-bleeding;   185
    But I'll amerce you with so strong a fine
    That you shall all repent the loss of mine:
    I will be deaf to pleading and excuses;
    Nor tears nor prayers shall purchase out abuses,
    Therefore use none: let Romeo hence in haste,   190
    Else, when he is found, that hour is his last.
    Bear hence this body, and attend our will:
    Mercy but murders, pardoning those that kill.

[Exeunt.]

PERSONA JOURNAL

How do these two deaths, Mercutio's and Tybalt's, affect you (emotionally, physically, financially, socially)?

185 **My blood:** my relative
186 **amerce:** punish

189 **purchase out abuses:** buy forgiveness

192 **attend our will:** come to hear my ruling
193 **Mercy . . . kill:** Being lenient with murderers simply leads to more murders.

PERSONA JOURNAL

From your point of view, do you think the Prince's verdict was fair? Why or why not?

Tone   The whole tone of *Romeo and Juliet* changes at the end of Act III, scene i. The mood until now has been one of romantic comedy, with joyous love scenes and hilarious fun. The mood of the rest of the play will be increasingly grim and tragic. Late in his career, Shakespeare wrote another play, *The Winter's Tale*, which is similarly divided in tone. Its first half is tragic, its second half comic and joyous.

Setting the Scene

ROMEO AND JULIET
Act III, scene ii *or* From Joy to Despair

Critical Query: How will Juliet react to the news of Romeo and Tybalt?

Classroom Set Design

This is the Capulet orchard set from Act II. There is standard Capulet/Montague divided seating with a bench or chairs upstage left.

Bench

Famous Quote from Scene ii

Give me my Romeo; and when he shall die
Take him and cut him out in little stars
and he will make the face of heaven so fine
That all the world will be in love with night . . .

From the Prop Box

- Rope for the rope ladder
- A flask or bottle for the Nurse's *aqua vita*
- A ring for Juliet to send to Romeo

In Character: Juliet in Turmoil

Juliet takes an emotional roller coaster ride through this scene, beginning with her excited anticipation of Romeo's arrival to her despair at his banishment. Plot her highs and lows on a graph like the one shown, using line numbers from the text to indicate her mood swings.

HIGHS Line ___ ___ ___ ___

LOWS Line ___ ___ ___

Warm-up Improv: Mixed Emotions

You did not make the gymnastics team, but your best friend did. Someone rushes in with the news that your friend has broken an	ankle and that as first alternate, you will now be on the team. How do you react? to the bearer of the news? to your friend?

Juliet is alone in the Capulet orchard, blissfully happy about her marriage to Romeo. She is eager for nightfall and the arrival of her new husband to her bedchamber.

Scene ii. Capulet's Orchard.

[Enter JULIET.*]*

✱ JULIET. Gallop apace, you fiery-footed steeds,
Towards Phoebus' lodging; such a waggoner
As Phaeton would whip you to the west
And bring in cloudy night immediately.—
Spread thy close curtain, love-performing night!   5
That runaways' eyes may wink, and Romeo
Leap to these arms, untalk'd of and unseen.—
Lovers can see to do their amorous rites
By their own beauties: or, if love be blind,
It best agrees with night.—Come, civil night,   10
Thou sober-suited matron, all in black,
And learn me how to lose a winning match,
Play'd for a pair of stainless maidenhoods:
Hood my unmann'd blood, bating in my cheeks,
With thy black mantle; till strange love, grown bold,   15
Think true love acted simple modesty.
Come, night;—come, Romeo;—come, thou day in night;
For thou wilt lie upon the wings of night
Whiter than new snow upon a raven's back.—
Come, gentle night;—come, loving, black-brow'd night,   20
Give me my Romeo; and, when he shall die,
Take him and cut him out in little stars,
And he will make the face of heaven so fine
That all the world will be in love with night,
And pay no worship to the garish sun.—   25
O, I have bought the mansion of a love,
But not possess'd it; and, though I am sold,

1–4 Juliet wants night (and therefore, Romeo) to come more quickly. She wishes that the sun god's son Phaeton, who was unable to control his father's chariot horses, would drive recklessly toward the sun and bring darkness on immediately.

6 runaways: unwanted observers; **wink:** close their eyes to what's happening

10 civil: courteous

11 sober-suited: gravely dressed

12 learn: teach

14 Hood my . . . mantle: Hide the wild blood fluttering in my cheeks. Juliet uses falconry images to describe her feelings. An untrained (**unmann'd**) falcon has a hood (**mantle**) put over its head to stop it from fluttering (**bating**) its wings

25 garish: gaudy

❓ What might Juliet be doing during this long speech?

✱ "Gallop apace, you fiery-footed steeds . . . " One of Shakespeare's favorite books was *Metamorphoses*, by the Roman poet Ovid (43 B.C.–17 A.D.). Shakespeare learned the story of Phaeton (and his disastrous race across the sky in his father Phoebus' sun chariot) from this collection of classical myths. He read Ovid in the original Latin, but also in a popular translation by Arthur Golding, who describes Apollo's (Phoebus') horses as "fiery-footed" and Phaeton as a "wagoner."

The Nurse enters with the rope ladder, and Juliet instantly realizes that something is very wrong. The Nurse gasps out that there has been a death.

Not yet enjoy'd: so tedious is this day
As is the night before some festival
To an impatient child that hath new robes,   30
And may not wear them. O, here comes my nurse,
And she brings news; and every tongue that speaks
But Romeo's name speaks heavenly eloquence.—

30 robes: clothes

[Enter NURSE, *with cords.]*

Now, nurse, what news? What hast thou there? the cords
That Romeo bid thee fetch?

NURSE.   Ay, ay, the cords.   35

[Throws them down.]

JULIET. Ah me! what news? why dost thou wring thy hands?

NURSE. Ah, well-a-day! he's dead, he's dead, he's dead!
We are undone, lady, we are undone!—
Alack the day!—he's gone, he's kill'd, he's dead!

37 well-a-day: alas

Emily Woolf as Juliet

From the Nurse's wailing, Juliet determines that Romeo is dead and begins to grieve. But then the Nurse says Tybalt's name.

JULIET. Can heaven be so envious?

NURSE.   Romeo can,   40
      Though heaven cannot.—O Romeo, Romeo!—
      Who ever would have thought it?—Romeo!

JULIET. What devil art thou, that dost torment me thus?
      This torture should be roar'd in dismal hell.
      Hath Romeo slain himself? say thou but 'Ay,'   45
      And that bare vowel "I" shall poison more
  ✱   Than the death-darting eye of cockatrice:
      I am not I if there be such an 'I,'
      Or those eyes shut that make thee answer 'Ay.'
      If he be slain, say 'Ay,' or if not, 'No.'   50
      Brief sounds determine of my weal or woe.

NURSE. I saw the wound, I saw it with mine eyes,—
      God save the mark!—here on his manly breast.
      A piteous corse, a bloody piteous corse;
      Pale, pale as ashes, all bedaub'd in blood,   55
      All in gore-blood;—I swounded at the sight.

JULIET. O, break, my heart!—poor bankrout, break at once!
      To prison, eyes; ne'er look on liberty!
      Vile earth, to earth resign; end motion here;
      And thou and Romeo press one heavy bier!   60

NURSE. O Tybalt, Tybalt, the best friend I had!
      O courteous Tybalt! honest gentleman!
      That ever I should live to see thee dead!

45 Even as she despairs over Romeo, Juliet plays with the meaning of the words *I* and *ay*.
47 cockatrice: a mythical creature that killed with a glance

51 weal or woe: happiness or sorrow

53 God save the mark: God protect me.
54 corse: body or corpse
55 bedaub'd: covered
56 swounded: fainted

❓ Why do you think the Nurse continues to let Juliet believe that Romeo is dead?
57 bankrout: bankrupt
59 Vile . . . bier: Wretched body, stop all human activity (**motion**), resign yourself to die, and share a burial slab (**bier**) with Romeo.

❓ Do you think the Nurse was actually best friends with Tybalt? Why would she say this?

✱ **Yum Yum!** "Roast cockatrice" was a popular dish in Medieval England. It was not made from an actual cockatrice (said to be part bird, part serpent, and part rooster), which would be dangerous (to say nothing of impossible) to catch. Instead, it was made from pig and rooster parts stitched together. Although the popularity of roast cockatrice may have waned by Shakespeare's time, he made references to the mythical creature in several of his plays.

Juliet now thinks both Tybalt and Romeo are dead. The Nurse finally manages to explain that Romeo has been banished for killing Tybalt. Juliet wonders how villainy and sweetness could be found in the same person.

JULIET. What storm is this that blows so contrary?
    Is Romeo slaughter'd, and is Tybalt dead?   65
    My dear-lov'd cousin, and my dearer lord?—
  ✽ Then, dreadful trumpet, sound the general doom!
    For who is living, if those two are gone?

NURSE. Tybalt is gone, and Romeo banished;
    Romeo that kill'd him, he is banished.   70

JULIET. O God!—did Romeo's hand shed Tybalt's blood?

NURSE. It did, it did; alas the day, it did!

JULIET. O serpent heart, hid with a flowering face!
    Did ever dragon keep so fair a cave?
    Beautiful tyrant! fiend angelical!   75
    Dove-feather'd raven! wolvish-ravening lamb!
    Despised substance of divinest show!
    Just opposite to what thou justly seem'st,
    A damned saint, an honourable villain!—
    O nature, what hadst thou to do in hell   80
    When thou didst bower the spirit of a fiend
    In mortal paradise of such sweet flesh?—
    Was ever book containing such vile matter
    So fairly bound? O, that deceit should dwell
    In such a gorgeous palace!

NURSE.   There's no trust,   85
    No faith, no honesty in men; all perjur'd,
    All forsworn, all naught, all dissemblers.—

67 dreadful trumpet: refers to the religious belief that the sound of a trumpet will announce doomsday, the end of the world

? Juliet now describes Romeo with a series of oxymorons—contradictory phrases or words such as "beautiful tyrant." Why does she use this kind of language to express her feelings about Romeo at this point?

78 justly: rightly

81 didst bower the spirit of a fiend: did let the devil in

86 all perjur'd: all liars
87 All forsworn . . . dissemblers: all break their word, all wicked, all hypocrites

? Do you think the Nurse really feels this way about men?

✽ **Shakespeare's Bible** When Juliet exclaims, "dreadful trumpet, sound the general doom!" she is referring to 1 Corinthians, 15:52. The Bible that Shakespeare knew (and knew very well) was the Geneva Bible, translated by English Protestants exiled in Switzerland during the Catholic reign of Mary I (1553–58). Shakespeare lived to see the publication of the King James Bible (1611). Some people believe he helped compose the Psalms for that version.

The Nurse expresses anger at Romeo, but Juliet defends him. She considers her unhappy situation—a relative dead and a husband of only three hours banished.

✱ Ah, where's my man? Give me some *aqua vitae.*—
These griefs, these woes, these sorrows make me old.
Shame come to Romeo!

JULIET. Blister'd be thy tongue   90
For such a wish! he was not born to shame:
Upon his brow shame is asham'd to sit;
For 'tis a throne where honour may be crown'd
Sole monarch of the universal earth.
O, what a beast was I to chide at him!   95

NURSE. Will you speak well of him that kill'd your cousin?

JULIET. Shall I speak ill of him that is my husband?
Ah, poor my lord, what tongue shall smooth thy name,
When I, thy three-hours' wife, have mangled it?—
But wherefore, villain, didst thou kill my cousin?   100
That villain cousin would have kill'd my husband:
Back, foolish tears, back to your native spring;
Your tributary drops belong to woe,
Which you, mistaking, offer up to joy.
My husband lives, that Tybalt would have slain;   105
And Tybalt's dead, that would have slain my husband:
All this is comfort; wherefore weep I, then?
Some word there was, worser than Tybalt's death,
That murder'd me: I would forget it fain;
But O, it presses to my memory   110
Like damnèd guilty deeds to sinners' minds:
'Tybalt is dead, and Romeo banished.'
That 'banishèd,' that one word 'banishèd,'
Hath slain ten thousand Tybalts. Tybalt's death
Was woe enough, if it had ended there: 115

95 chide: scold

103 Your tributary . . . woe: Your tears are for sorrow

? When the Nurse agrees with Juliet about men's wickedness, Juliet suddenly reverses herself and begins to defend Romeo. Why does she do this?

✱ **Medieval Moonshine**   Alchemists were chemist-magicians who tried to turn common metals into gold. When they practiced distillation (the separation of liquids), they found that they could make highly alcoholic liquids, now called liquor. The alchemists thought that these liquids had magical powers, so they called them *aqua vitae*—Latin for "water of life." The *aqua vitae* that the Nurse calls for is brandy.

Juliet laments Romeo's banishment and speaks of ending her life. The Nurse becomes alarmed, and offers to find Romeo and bring him to say good-bye.

Or, if sour woe delights in fellowship,
And needly will be rank'd with other griefs,—
Why follow'd not, when she said 'Tybalt's dead,'
Thy father, or thy mother, nay, or both,
Which modern lamentation might have mov'd?   120
But with a rear-ward following Tybalt's death,
'Romeo is banishèd'—to speak that word
Is father, mother, Tybalt, Romeo, Juliet,
All slain, all dead: 'Romeo is banishèd,'—
There is no end, no limit, measure, bound,   125
In that word's death; no words can that woe sound.—
Where is my father and my mother, nurse?

NURSE. Weeping and wailing over Tybalt's corse:
   Will you go to them? I will bring you thither.

JULIET. Wash they his wounds with tears: mine shall be spent,   130
   When theirs are dry, for Romeo's banishment.
   Take up those cords. Poor ropes, you are beguil'd,
   Both you and I; for Romeo is exil'd:
   He made you for a highway to my bed;
   But I, a maid, die maiden-widowèd.   135
   Come, cords; come, nurse; I'll to my wedding-bed;
   And death, not Romeo, take my maidenhead!

NURSE. Hie to your chamber. I'll find Romeo
   To comfort you: I wot well where he is.
   Hark ye, your Romeo will be here at night: 140
   I'll to him; he is hid at Lawrence' cell.

JULIET. O, find him! Give this ring to my true knight,
   And bid him come to take his last farewell.

[Exeunt.]

116–117 if sour . . . griefs: if misery loves company and must be accompanied by other sorrows
118–125 If I'd heard that my parents were dead along with Tybalt, I would have experienced normal grief (**modern lamentation**). But when "Tybalt's dead" is followed (**rear-ward**) by "Romeo is banished," then it's as if we are all dead and grief is limitless.

129 bring you thither: take you there

132 beguil'd: cheated, robbed

❓ Why does the Nurse offer to find Romeo and bring him to Juliet?

138 Hie: hurry
139 wot: know

Setting the Scene

ROMEO AND JULIET
Act III, scene iii *or* Look on the Bright Side

Critical Query: How will Romeo react to his exile?

Classroom Set Design

This is the set-up for the Friar's cell that was used in Act II, scene vi. There is Capulet/Montague divided seating, with a bench or chairs used as an altar downstage left.

Altar

Time Capsule: Friendly Friar

Friar Lawrence is a member of the Franciscan Order of Friars, a Roman Catholic order founded in 1209 by St. Francis of Assisi. Franciscan friars took a vow of poverty and had to work for a living. Even so, they were revered by both rich and poor in Renaissance cities like Verona. So it is not surprising that Friar Lawrence is highly respected by everyone in Verona, including the Prince—nor that he has to grow herbs to make ends meet.

Word Play: Repetition

The repetition of words and phrases is one of Shakespeare's favorite ways of increasing the tension and emotional impact of a speech or scene. Occasionally repetition may have a quite different effect. Review the Friar's speech on pages 128–130. Jot down the repeated words and phrases you find. Which of the Friar's qualities might be highlighted by this repetition? Where else in the scene do you find repetition? What does this technique add to the scene?

From the Prop Box

- A sword for Romeo
- A ring

In Character: Romeo in Turmoil

Review the graph of Juliet's emotions that you plotted for the preceding scene. Draw the same kind of diagram for Romeo in this scene. How does the comparison of these two graphs help to answer the Critical Query above?

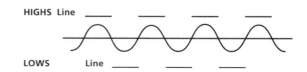

HIGHS Line _____   _____   _____   _____

LOWS   Line _____   _____   _____   _____

Warm-up Improv: Good News or Bad?

Two neighbors are discussing the situation after a flood has done a great deal of damage to their homes. One is a complete optimist; the other a complete pessimist.

Romeo has taken refuge at Friar Lawrence's cell, where he learns that the Prince has banished him. Instead of seeing this as merciful, however, Romeo claims that death would be preferable.

Scene iii. Friar Lawrence's Cell

[*Enter* FRIAR LAWRENCE.]

FRIAR. Romeo, come forth; come forth, thou fearful man.
    Affliction is enamour'd of thy parts,
    And thou art wedded to calamity.

[*Enter* ROMEO.]

ROMEO. Father, what news? What is the prince's doom
    What sorrow craves acquaintance at my hand,   5
    That I yet know not?

FRIAR.   Too familiar
    Is my dear son with such sour company:
    I bring thee tidings of the prince's doom.

ROMEO. What less than doomsday is the prince's doom?

FRIAR. A gentler judgment vanish'd from his lips,—   10
    Not body's death, but body's banishment.

ROMEO. Ha, banishment? be merciful, say 'death;'
    For exile hath more terror in his look,
    Much more than death; do not say 'banishment.'

FRIAR. Hence from Verona art thou banishèd: 15
    Be patient, for the world is broad and wide.

ROMEO. There is no world without Verona walls,
    But purgatory, torture, hell itself.
    Hence banishèd is banish'd from the world,
    And world's exile is death,—then 'banishèd'   20
    Is death mis-term'd: calling death 'banishment,'
    Thou cutt'st my head off with a golden axe,
    And smil'st upon the stroke that murders me.

2 affliction is . . . parts: trouble loves you

4 doom: sentence

5–6 What . . . not: What other problems are there that I don't know about yet?

9 doomsday: death

10 vanish'd: came

17 without: outside of

20–23 then . . . me: banished is just another word for death (**death mis-term'd**). Using the word "banished" is the same as killing me with a golden axe and smiling while you do it. I'm still dead, no matter what the weapon's made of.

❓ Why does Romeo think banishment is worse than death? What mental state does he seem to be in?

The Friar is surprised at Romeo's disregard for the Prince's mercy, but Romeo continues to despair at being separated from Juliet.

FRIAR. O deadly sin! O rude unthankfulness!
Thy fault our law calls death; but the kind prince,   25
Taking thy part, hath rushed aside the law,
And turn'd that black word 'death' to 'banishment':
This is dear mercy, and thou see'st it not.

ROMEO. 'Tis torture, and not mercy: heaven is here,
✱ Where Juliet lives; and every cat, and dog,   30
And little mouse, every unworthy thing,
Live here in heaven, and may look on her;
But Romeo may not.—More validity,
More honourable state, more courtship lives
In carrion flies than Romeo: they may seize   35
On the white wonder of dear Juliet's hand,
And steal immortal blessing from her lips;
Who, even in pure and vestal modesty,
Still blush, as thinking their own kisses sin;
But Romeo may not; he is banishèd,—   40
This may flies do, when I from this must fly;
They are free men, but I am banishèd;
And sayest thou yet that exile is not death!
Hadst thou no poison mix'd, no sharp-ground knife,
No sudden mean of death, though ne'er so mean,   45
But 'banishèd' to kill me; 'banishèd'?
O friar, the damned use that word in hell;
Howlings attend it: how hast thou the heart,
Being a divine, a ghostly confessor,
A sin-absolver, and my friend profess'd,   50
To mangle me with that word 'banishèd'?

FRIAR. Thou fond mad man, hear me speak a little,—

ROMEO. O, thou wilt speak again of banishment.

25 Thy fault . . . death: The penalty is death for what you did.

28 dear: true

33 validity: value

35 carrion flies: flies that feed on dead flesh

38 vestal: virginal

51 mangle: wound

52 fond: foolish

✱ **". . . and every cat, and dog, / And little mouse . . . may look on her . . . "** Shakespeare here refers to the old saying, "A cat may look at a king." Years after writing *Romeo and Juliet*, Shakespeare echoed Romeo's sense of injustice in his tragedy *King Lear*. When Lear's beloved daughter Cordelia is slain, he exclaims over her body, "Why should a dog, a horse, a rat, have life, / And thou no breath at all?"

Romeo in Friar Lawrence's cell (Zeffirelli, 1968)

Romeo refuses to listen to any comforting words, and claims that the Friar cannot possibly understand how he feels. A knocking is heard, and the Friar urges Romeo to hide.

FRIAR. I'll give thee armour to keep off that word;
    Adversity's sweet milk, philosophy,   55
    To comfort thee, though thou art banishèd.

ROMEO. Yet 'banishèd'? Hang up philosophy!
    Unless philosophy can make a Juliet,
    Displant a town, reverse a prince's doom,
    It helps not, it prevails not,—talk no more.   60

FRIAR. O, then I see that madmen have no ears.

ROMEO. How should they, when that wise men have no eyes?

FRIAR. Let me dispute with thee of thy estate.

ROMEO. Thou canst not speak of that thou dost not feel:
    Wert thou as young as I, Juliet thy love,   65
    An hour but married, Tybalt murderèd,
    Doting like me, and like me banishèd,
    Then mightst thou speak, then mightst thou tear thy hair,
    And fall upon the ground, as I do now,
    Taking the measure of an unmade grave.   70

[Knocking within.]

FRIAR. Arise; one knocks. Good Romeo, hide thyself.

ROMEO. Not I; unless the breath of heartsick groans,
    Mist-like infold me from the search of eyes.

[Knocking.]

FRIAR. Hark, how they knock!—Who's there?—Romeo, arise;
    Thou wilt be taken.—Stay awhile;—Stand up;   75

[Knocking.]

    Run to my study.—By-and-by!—God's will!
    What simpleness is this.—I come, I come!

54 to keep off: to protect you from

59 displant: move

63 Let . . . estate: Let me discuss (**dispute**) your situation (**estate**) with you.
65 Wert: if you were

70 Taking . . . grave: stretched out to fit the grave I'll soon be in

73 Mist-like infold me: hides me in a mist

? What do you think of Romeo's behavior?

The Nurse enters and asks for Romeo, who is on the ground weeping. She scolds him, saying he needs to be a man for Juliet's sake. Romeo asks how his love is faring.

[Knocking.]

    Who knocks so hard? whence come you? what's your will?

NURSE. *[Within.]* Let me come in, and you shall know my errand;
    I come from Lady Juliet.

FRIAR.   Welcome then.   80

[Enter NURSE.]

NURSE. O holy friar, O, tell me, holy friar,
    Where is my lady's lord, where's Romeo?

FRIAR. There on the ground, with his own tears made drunk.

NURSE. O, he is even in my mistress' case,—
    Just in her case! O woeful sympathy!   85
    Piteous predicament! Even so lies she,
    Blubbering and weeping, weeping and blubbering.—
    Stand up, stand up; stand, an you be a man:
    For Juliet's sake, for her sake, rise and stand;
    Why should you fall into so deep an O?   90

ROMEO. Nurse! *[He rises.]*

NURSE. Ah sir! ah sir!—Well, death's the end of all.

ROMEO. Spakest thou of Juliet? how is it with her?
    Doth not she think me an old murderer,
    Now I have stain'd the childhood of our joy   95
    With blood remov'd but little from her own?
    Where is she? and how doth she! and what says
    My conceal'd lady to our cancell'd love?

84 even in my . . . her case: just like my mistress—just like her!
85 woeful sympathy: sympathetic grief

❓ Knowing how upset the Nurse was at Romeo, are you surprised that she appears to be sympathetic here?
90 O: an expression of grief

94 old: hardened

96 With blood . . . own: with blood (Tybalt's) from someone close to her
98 conceal'd: secretly married

The Nurse relates that Juliet is distraught. Romeo, with the belief that he is the cause of Juliet's grief, draws his sword to kill himself. The Friar stops him and scolds him for thinking of such an act.

NURSE. O, she says nothing, sir, but weeps and weeps;
    And now falls on her bed; and then starts up,   100
    And Tybalt calls; and then on Romeo cries,
    And then down falls again.

ROMEO.   As if that name,
    Shot from the deadly level of a gun,
    Did murder her; as that name's cursèd hand
    Murder'd her kinsman.—O, tell me, friar, tell me,   105
    In what vile part of this anatomy
    Doth my name lodge? tell me, that I may sack
    The hateful mansion.

[Drawing his sword.]

FRIAR.   Hold thy desperate hand:
✻ Art thou a man? thy form cries out thou art;
    Thy tears are womanish; thy wild acts denote   110
    The unreasonable fury of a beast;
    Unseemly woman in a seeming man!
    Or ill-beseeming beast in seeming both!
    Thou hast amaz'd me: by my holy order,
    I thought thy disposition better temper'd.   115
    Hast thou slain Tybalt? wilt thou slay thyself?
    And slay thy lady, too, that lives in thee,
    By doing damnèd hate upon thyself?
    Why rail'st thou on thy birth, the heaven, and earth?
    Since birth and heaven and earth, all three do meet   120
    In thee at once; which thou at once wouldst lose.
    Fie, fie, thou sham'st thy shape, thy love, thy wit;
    Which, like a usurer, abound'st in all,

---

103 level: aim

106 anatomy: body
107–108 sack the hateful mansion: destroy my cursed body

113 ill-beseeming: unbecoming

115 temper'd: mixed

118 By doing . . . thyself: by killing yourself, which is a sin that will damn your soul
119 rail'st thou on . . . earth: ranting about your existence, soul, and body
121 at once wouldst lose: Since Friar Lawrence is Catholic, he believes that Romeo would lose his soul as well as his earthly life if he committed suicide.
122 sham'st thy shape: shame your body
123 usurer: moneylender

✻ **Source Material**   When Friar Lawrence attacks Romeo's manhood, his words are strikingly close to those of Shakespeare's source—the poem *Romeus and Juliet* by Arthur Brooke: " 'Art thou,' quoth he, 'a man? thy shape saith so thou art:/ Thy crying and thy weeping eyes denote [show] a woman's heart.' " This is far from the only place where Shakespeare's words closely echo Brooke's poem and other works.

The Friar enumerates the reasons Romeo should be happy instead of depressed, and urges him to spend the night with Juliet. Early the next morning, however, Romeo must hurry away to Mantua where he will stay during his exile.

And usest none in that true use indeed
Which should bedeck thy shape, thy love, thy wit: 125
Thy noble shape is but a form of wax,
Digressing from the valour of a man;
Thy dear love sworn, but hollow perjury,
Killing that love which thou hast vow'd to cherish;
Thy wit, that ornament to shape and love,   130
Mis-shapen in the conduct of them both,
✱ Like powder in a skilless soldier's flask,
Is set a-fire by thine own ignorance,
And thou dismember'd with thine own defence.
What, rouse thee, man! thy Juliet is alive,   135
For whose dear sake thou wast but lately dead;
There art thou happy: Tybalt would kill thee,
But thou slewest Tybalt; there art thou happy too:
The law, that threaten'd death, becomes thy friend,
And turns it to exile; there art thou happy: 140
A pack of blessings lights upon thy back;
Happiness courts thee in her best array;
But, like a misbehav'd and sullen wench,
Thou pout'st upon thy fortune and thy love:—
Take heed, take heed, for such die miserable.   145
Go, get thee to thy love, as was decreed,
Ascend her chamber, hence and comfort her:
But, look, thou stay not till the watch be set,
For then thou canst not pass to Mantua;
Where thou shalt live till we can find a time   150
To blaze your marriage, reconcile your friends,
Beg pardon of the prince, and call thee back
With twenty hundred thousand times more joy

126–127 Thy noble . . . man: You're acting like a wax dummy that has no manly courage.

135 What, rouse thee: Wake up

143 sullen wench: melancholy girl
144 pout'st: frown

148 the watch be set: the night watchmen come on duty at the city gates
149 Mantua: a town approximately 30 miles from Verona
151 blaze: announce

Handle with Care Match-lock guns were common in Shakespeare's time, so-called because a lighted match was used to set off the firing mechanism (the "lock"). Although they were the first guns to use triggers, match-locks were clumsy weapons and dangerous to use. The gunner had to be careful not to accidentally ignite the glass container ("flask") in which he stored his gunpowder. This would cause an explosion that could injure or kill him.

The Nurse marvels at the Friar's wisdom and then leaves to prepare Juliet for Romeo's visit. Friar Lawrence promises to keep Romeo informed while he is in Mantua.

Than thou went'st forth in lamentation.—
Go before, nurse: commend me to thy lady;   155
And bid her hasten all the house to bed,
Which heavy sorrow makes them apt unto.
Romeo is coming.

157 apt unto: inclined to do

NURSE. O Lord, I could have stay'd here all the night
To hear good counsel: O, what learning is!—   160
My lord, I'll tell my lady you will come.

ROMEO. Do so, and bid my sweet prepare to chide.

162 chide: scold me

NURSE. Here, sir, a ring she bid me give you, sir:
Hie you, make haste, for it grows very late.

[Exit.]

ROMEO. How well my comfort is reviv'd by this!   165

165 well my comfort is reviv'd: I am comforted

* FRIAR. Go hence; good night! and here stands all your state:
Either be gone before the watch be set,
Or by the break of day disguis'd from hence.
Sojourn in Mantua; I'll find out your man,
And he shall signify from time to time   170
Every good hap to you that chances here:
Give me thy hand; 'tis late; farewell; good night.

166 stands at your state: is your situation
167–171 Either . . . Mantua: Either leave before the night watchmen come on duty or leave at daybreak in disguise. Stay (**sojourn**) in Mantua. I'll contact your servant and he'll let you know (**signify**) about any positive developments (**hap**) that happen here.

ROMEO. But that a joy past joy calls out on me,
It were a grief so brief to part with thee:
Farewell.   175

[Exeunt.]

* **Decisions, Decisions**   Romeo may be one of Shakespeare's most charming and poetic heroes, but he's by no means the most decisive. Many times throughout the play, other characters have to tell him what to do. Here, the Friar must encourage him to spend his wedding night with Juliet! As you read the play, ask yourself what decisions Romeo *does* make for himself. How do those decisions work out?

Setting the Scene

ROMEO AND JULIET

Act III, scenes iv and v *or* What's a Girl to Do?

Critical Query: How do Juliet's actions differ from what is expected of her?

Classroom Set Design

Seats will be pushed together as closely as possible to allow for aisles on either side of the room. The aisle nearest to Juliet's bed will serve as the balcony where Romeo escapes. He might climb over a desk to represent his descent down the rope ladder. The other aisle will be used for entrances and exits of the other characters in the scenes. The teacher's desk will be placed upstage right and will represent a chest or table in scene iv and Juliet's bed in scene v.

Desk · Acting Area · Balcony · Entrance

Behind the Scene: Lord Capulet in the Hot Seat

Early in the play, Lord Capulet appeared to be a doting and indulgent father. In scene v, however, he shows a completely different side. Pay careful attention to his comments about and to Juliet. When the scene ends, the actor playing Lord Capulet must sit in the "hot seat" and be questioned about his actions by class members.

From the Prop Box

Rope ladder

In Character: Juliet & Company

Juliet's relationship with many characters changes in these scenes. Fill in a relationship chart like the one below to see who is a friend and who is an enemy at the end of scene v.

Character	Beginning of Scene	End of Scene
Romeo	Friend	Friend
Lord Capulet		
Lady Capulet		
Nurse		

Warm-up Improv: Conflict of Interest

Your parents have a big surprise for you! They've enrolled you at a very prestigious boarding school for your senior year—practically guaranteeing you a spot at a top university. You are stunned! This is the last thing you want, and your parents can't understand how you could be so ungrateful.

Paris has been paying his respects to Lord and Lady Capulet. Lord Capulet explains that Juliet has been overcome with grief since the death of Tybalt, and therefore talk of marriage has been put on hold. As Paris prepares to leave, Lord Capulet changes his mind.

Scene iv. A Room in Capulet's House

[Enter CAPULET, LADY CAPULET, *and* PARIS.*]*

CAPULET. Things have fallen out, sir, so unluckily
   That we have had no time to move our daughter:
✹ Look you, she lov'd her kinsman Tybalt dearly,
   And so did I; well, we were born to die.
   'Tis very late; she'll not come down to-night: 5
   I promise you, but for your company,
   I would have been a-bed an hour ago.

PARIS. These times of woe afford no times to woo.—
   Madam, good night: commend me to your daughter.

LADY CAPULET. I will, and know her mind early to-morrow;   10
   To-night she's mew'd up to her heaviness.

CAPULET. Sir Paris, I will make a desperate tender
   Of my child's love: I think she will be rul'd
   In all respects by me; nay more, I doubt it not.—
   Wife, go you to her ere you go to bed;   15
   Acquaint her here of my son Paris' love;
   And bid her, mark you me, on Wednesday next,—
   But, soft! what day is this?

PARIS.   Monday, my lord.

CAPULET. Monday! ha, ha! Well, Wednesday is too soon,
   Thursday let it be;—a Thursday, tell her,   20
   She shall be married to this noble earl.—
   Will you be ready? do you like this haste?
   We'll keep no great ado,—a friend or two;
   For, hark you, Tybalt being slain so late,
   It may be thought we held him carelessly,   25

1 fallen out: happened
2 move: influence

9 commend me: give my regards

11 mew'd up to her heaviness: taken to her room with grief
12 desperate tender: bold offer

16 my son: my son-in-law to be

20 a: on

23 keep no great ado: won't go to much trouble
24 late: recently
25 held him so carelessly: didn't respect him very much

✹ **Irony** How *ironic* it is that Lord Capulet thinks that Juliet is grieving over Tybalt's death! (Remember, *irony* is when appearances are somehow at odds with reality.) How do you think he would react if he knew that Juliet is married to Romeo? Some critics have suggested that he might actually be pleased, and that it is a fatal mistake for Romeo, Juliet, the Friar, and the Nurse to keep the marriage a secret. Do you agree?

Paris eagerly accepts the Thursday wedding date, and Lord Capulet commands Lady Capulet to tell Juliet of his decision.

Being our kinsman, if we revel much:
Therefore we'll have some half a dozen friends,
And there an end. But what say you to Thursday?

✳ PARIS. My lord, I would that Thursday were to-morrow.

CAPULET. Well, get you gone: o' Thursday be it then.—   30
Go you to Juliet, ere you go to bed,
Prepare her, wife, against this wedding-day.—
Farewell, my lord.—Light to my chamber, ho!—
Afore me, it is so very very late
That we may call it early by and by.—   35
Good night.

[Exeunt.]

32 **against:** for

34 **Afore me:** mild exclamation meaning 'by my life' or 'indeed.'
35 **by and by:** soon

❓ What do you think Juliet's reaction will be to this arranged marriage? What will she do and say?

✳ **Doubling** Paris is certainly an easygoing man who seems perfectly willing to agree to anything Lord Capulet proposes. How different he is from the late, hot-headed Mercutio! And yet, at least one scholar has suggested that Mercutio and Paris were originally played by the same actor. The practice of giving more than one role to the same actor is called *doubling*, and it was common on Shakespeare's stage.

It is the morning after Romeo and Juliet's marriage. They have spent the night together in Juliet's bedroom. As they wake, Romeo says he must leave before dawn.

Scene v. An Open Gallery to Juliet's Chamber, Overlooking the Orchard

[Enter ROMEO *and* JULIET.*]*

JULIET. Wilt thou be gone? it is not yet near day:
    It was the nightingale, and not the lark,
    That pierc'd the fearful hollow of thine ear;
    Nightly she sings on yond pomegranate tree:
    Believe me, love, it was the nightingale.   5

ROMEO. It was the lark, the herald of the morn,
    No nightingale: look, love, what envious streaks
    Do lace the severing clouds in yonder east:
    Night's candles are burnt out, and jocund day
    Stands tiptoe on the misty mountain tops.   10
    I must be gone and live, or stay and die.

It is daybreak, but Juliet wants to pretend that it's still night so Romeo can stay longer. The nightingale's song is associated with the night; the lark's song with dawn.

1 Wilt: must

7–8 Look . . . clouds: Look at how those hateful (**envious**) streaks of daylight twine (**lace**) through the scattering (**severing**) clouds.
9 Night's candles: stars; **jocund:** cheerful

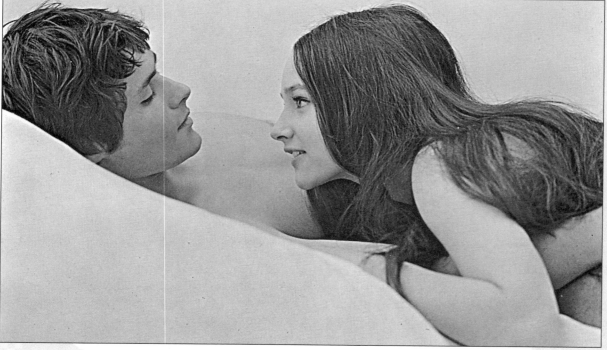

Romeo and Juliet in her chamber (Zeffirelli, 1968)

Juliet, not wanting Romeo to leave, pretends it is not day. Romeo is willing to go along with this game, but Juliet becomes frightened at the thought of him being caught. As Juliet urges Romeo to leave, the Nurse enters.

JULIET. Yond light is not daylight, I know it, I:
　　It is some meteor that the sun exhales
　　To be to thee this night a torch-bearer
　　And light thee on the way to Mantua:　　　　　　15
　　Therefore stay yet, thou need'st not to be gone.

ROMEO. Let me be ta'en, let me be put to death;
　　I am content, so thou wilt have it so.
　　I'll say yon gray is not the morning's eye,
　　'Tis but the pale reflex of Cynthia's brow;　　　　20
　　Nor that is not the lark whose notes do beat
　　The vaulty heaven so high above our heads:
　　I have more care to stay than will to go.—
　　Come, death, and welcome! Juliet wills it so.—
　　How is't, my soul? let's talk,—it is not day.　　　25

JULIET. It is, it is!—hie hence, be gone, away!
　　It is the lark that sings so out of tune,
　　Straining harsh discords and unpleasing sharps.
　　Some say the lark makes sweet division;
　　This doth not so, for she divideth us:　　　　　　30
✱　Some say the lark and loathèd toad change eyes;
　　O, now I would they had chang'd voices too!
　　Since arm from arm that voice doth us affray,
　　Hunting thee hence with hunt's-up to the day.
　　O, now be gone; more light and light it grows.　　35

ROMEO. More light and light,—more dark and dark our woes!

[Enter NURSE.]

What would have happened to Romeo if he had been discovered in Juliet's room?

17 ta'en: taken, captured

19 morning's eye: beginning of dawn
20 reflex: reflection; **Cynthia's brow:** Cynthia (Diana), goddess of the moon, was sometimes depicted as having a crescent moon on her forehead.
21–22 notes do beat the vaulty heaven: songs rise up to the valted heavens
23 care: desire

29 division: melody

31 loathèd: hated; **change:** exchanged

33 affray: frighten
34 hunt's-up to the day: the song that awakens hunters

✱ **"Some say the lark and loathèd toad change eyes . . . "** In Shakespeare's time, the lark's eyes were said to be ugly, the toad's eyes beautiful. So the lark and the toad were thought to have changed eyes. The toad's head was also said to contain a "toadstone"—a precious object which could be worn as a charm. In Shakespeare's *As You Like It*, a character observes, "Sweet are the uses of adversity, / Which, like the toad, ugly and venomous, / Wears yet a precious jewel in his head . . . "

The Nurse warns Juliet that Lady Capulet is coming. Romeo kisses Juliet and prepares to climb down the rope ladder.

NURSE. Madam!

JULIET. Nurse?

NURSE. Your lady mother is coming to your chamber:
The day is broke; be wary, look about.   40

[Exit.]

JULIET. Then, window, let day in, and let life out.

✱ **ROMEO.** Farewell, farewell! one kiss, and I'll descend.

[Descends.]

❓ Do you think the Nurse would be punished for knowing about and assisting with this rendezvous?

Romeo and Juliet,
Sir Frank Dicksee, 1884

✱ **The Great Escape**   Back in Act III, scene ii, the Nurse brought Juliet a rope ladder for Romeo to use to climb up to her window. In Shakespeare's original production, Romeo surely used this ladder to climb down from that window in this scene. Then Juliet hastily pulled the ladder back up to conceal it from her mother.

JULIET. Art thou gone so? my lord, my love, my friend!
I must hear from thee every day i' the hour,
For in a minute there are many days: 45
O, by this count I shall be much in years
Ere I again behold my Romeo!

ROMEO. Farewell!
I will omit no opportunity
That may convey my greetings, love, to thee.   50

JULIET. O, think'st thou we shall ever meet again?

ROMEO. I doubt it not; and all these woes shall serve
For sweet discourses in our time to come.

JULIET. O God! I have an ill-divining soul!
Methinks I see thee, now thou art below,   55
As one dead in the bottom of a tomb:
Either my eyesight fails, or thou look'st pale.

ROMEO. And trust me, love, in my eye so do you:
✱ Dry sorrow drinks our blood. Adieu, adieu!

[Exit below.]

JULIET. O fortune, fortune! all men call thee fickle: 60
If thou art fickle, what dost thou with him
That is renown'd for faith? Be fickle, fortune;
For then, I hope, thou wilt not keep him long
But send him back.

LADY CAPULET. [*Within.*]   Ho, daughter! are you up?

JULIET. Who is't that calls? is it my lady mother?   65
Is she not down so late, or up so early?
What unaccustom'd cause procures her hither?

44 **i':** on

46 **much in years:** very old

50 **convey:** send

53 **discourses:** conversations

54 **ill-divining soul:** feeling of doom

62 **renown'd:** well-known

67 **unaccustom'd cause . . . hither:** unusual event brings her here

✱ **Health Hazard**   Sighs of sadness were considered hazardous to one's health in Shakespeare's day. Every sigh was said to drain the heart of a drop of blood. So when Romeo tells Juliet, "Dry sorrow drinks our blood," he really means it. Do you remember the first scene of *Romeo and Juliet*, when Old Montague says of Romeo's melancholy, "Black and portentous must this humour prove"? Serious blood loss may have been one of Montague's worries.

Lady Capulet enters Juliet's room and mistakenly thinks that Juliet is sad because of Tybalt's death.

✱ *[Enter* LADY CAPULET.*]*

LADY CAPULET. Why, how now, Juliet?

JULIET.   Madam, I am not well.

LADY CAPULET. Evermore weeping for your cousin's death?
    What, wilt thou wash him from his grave with tears?   70
    An if thou couldst, thou couldst not make him live;
    Therefore have done: some grief shows much of love;
    But much of grief shows still some want of wit.

JULIET. Yet let me weep for such a feeling loss.   **74 feeling:** deeply felt

LADY CAPULET. So shall you feel the loss, but not the friend   75
    Which you weep for.

JULIET.   Feeling so the loss,
    I cannot choose but ever weep the friend.

LADY CAPULET. Well, girl, thou weep'st not so much for his death
    As that the villain lives which slaughter'd him.

JULIET. What villain, madam?

LADY CAPULET.   That same villain Romeo.   80

JULIET. *[Aside.]* Villain and he be many miles asunder.—   **81 asunder:** apart
    God pardon him! I do, with all my heart;
    And yet no man like he doth grieve my heart.

LADY CAPULET. That is because the traitor murderer lives.

JULIET. Ay, madam, from the reach of these my hands.   85
    Would none but I might venge my cousin's death!   **86 venge:** avenge

✱ **Enter Lady Capulet**   In Shakespeare's original production, Juliet had been standing in a window through the first part of this scene. Lady Capulet seems likely to have entered on the main stage below the window, calling, "Ho, daughter! are you up?" (The stage direction "[*Within.*]," added by an editor, is probably a mistake.) As quickly as possible, Juliet hurried down an interior stairway, then stepped out onto the stage to meet her mother.

During a conversation between Juliet and her mother, Juliet speaks about her feelings for Tybalt and Romeo in such a way that Lady Capulet hears one thing while Juliet means another. Lady Capulet tells Juliet that she is to marry Paris on Thursday.

LADY CAPULET. We will have vengeance for it, fear thou not:
✸ Then weep no more. I'll send to one in Mantua,—
Where that same banish'd runagate doth live,—
Shall give him such an unaccustom'd dram   90
That he shall soon keep Tybalt company:
And then I hope thou wilt be satisfied.

JULIET. Indeed I never shall be satisfied
With Romeo till I behold him—dead—
Is my poor heart so for a kinsman vex'd: 95
Madam, if you could find out but a man
To bear a poison, I would temper it,
That Romeo should, upon receipt thereof,
Soon sleep in quiet. O, how my heart abhors
To hear him nam'd,—and cannot come to him,—   100
To wreak the love I bore my cousin Tybalt
Upon his body that hath slaughter'd him!

LADY CAPULET. Find thou the means, and I'll find such a man.
But now I'll tell thee joyful tidings, girl.

JULIET. And joy comes well in such a needy time: 105
What are they, I beseech your ladyship?

LADY CAPULET. Well, well, thou hast a careful father, child;
One who, to put thee from thy heaviness,
Hath sorted out a sudden day of joy
That thou expect'st not, nor I look'd not for.   110

JULIET. Madam, in happy time, what day is that?

LADY CAPULET. Marry, my child, early next Thursday morn
The gallant, young, and noble gentleman,
The County Paris, at St. Peter's Church,
Shall happily make thee there a joyful bride.   115

89 runagate: outlaw

90 unaccustom'd dram: strong poison

97 temper: mix

99 abhors: hates

106 beseech: beg

107 careful: thoughtful

109 sorted out: selected

111 in happy time: for heaven's sake

✸ **Is She Clairvoyant?**   Realistically, there is no way that Lady Capulet would know that Romeo has fled to Mantua. All she could know is that he has been sent into exile. But this is probably not a true mistake on Shakespeare's part. Unlike today's authors and playwrights, he saw little need to worry over such realistic details.

Juliet insists that it is too soon to marry since Paris has not even come to woo her. Lord Capulet enters Juliet's chamber and is told that Juliet objects to her father's wishes.

JULIET. Now by Saint Peter's Church, and Peter too,
He shall not make me there a joyful bride.
I wonder at this haste; that I must wed
Ere he that should be husband comes to woo.
I pray you, tell my lord and father, madam,   120
I will not marry yet; and when I do, I swear
It shall be Romeo, whom you know I hate,
Rather than Paris:—these are news indeed!

LADY CAPULET. Here comes your father: tell him so yourself,
And see how he will take it at your hands.   125

[Enter CAPULET *and* NURSE.*]*

CAPULET. When the sun sets, the air doth drizzle dew;
But for the sunset of my brother's son
It rains downright.—
How now! a conduit, girl? what, still in tears?
Evermore showering? In one little body   130
✷ Thou counterfeit'st a bark, a sea, a wind:
For still thy eyes, which I may call the sea,
Do ebb and flow with tears; the bark thy body is,
Sailing in this salt flood; the winds, thy sighs;
Who,—raging with thy tears and they with them,—   135
Without a sudden calm, will overset
Thy tempest-tossèd body.—How now, wife!
Have you deliver'd to her our decree?

LADY CAPULET. Ay, sir; but she will none, she gives you thanks.
I would the fool were married to her grave!   140

CAPULET. Soft! take me with you, take me with you, wife.
How! will she none? doth she not give us thanks?

❓ Reread lines 64–125 between Juliet and Lady Capulet, and explain the double meanings in Juliet's words.

129 conduit: fountain

131 counterfeit'st a bark: act like a boat

141 soft: wait; **take me with you:** let me understand you

✷ **Conceit** A *conceit*, remember, is an extended comparison. Lord Capulet uses a conceit here in likening his daughter to a boat, a sea, and a wind. Does Capulet's fancy language strike you as a little out of character? Elsewhere, he speaks simply, directly, and bluntly. Perhaps young Shakespeare just couldn't resist yet another chance to show off his poetic skills.

Lord Capulet is outraged by his daughter's disobedience. Juliet attempts to explain that she does not love Paris, but Capulet threatens to drag her to the ceremony. Juliet pleads with her father.

Is she not proud? doth she not count her bles'd,
Unworthy as she is, that we have wrought
So worthy a gentleman to be her bridegroom?   145

JULIET. Not proud you have; but thankful that you have:
Proud can I never be of what I hate;
But thankful even for hate that is meant love.

CAPULET. How now, how now, chop-logic! What is this?
'Proud,'—and, 'I thank you,'—and 'I thank you not'—   150
And yet not proud:—mistress minion, you,
Thank me no thankings, nor proud me no prouds,
But fettle your fine joints 'gainst Thursday next
To go with Paris to Saint Peter's Church,
Or I will drag thee on a hurdle thither.   155
Out, you green-sickness carrion! out, you baggage!
You tallow-face!

✳ **LADY CAPULET.**   Fie, fie! what, are you mad?

JULIET. Good father, I beseech you on my knees,
Hear me with patience but to speak a word.

CAPULET. Hang thee, young baggage! disobedient wretch!   160
I tell thee what,—get thee to church o' Thursday,
Or never after look me in the face:
Speak not, reply not, do not answer me;
My fingers itch.—Wife, we scarce thought us bles'd
That God had lent us but this only child;   165
But now I see this one is one too much,
And that we have a curse in having her:
Out on her, hilding!

NURSE.   God in heaven bless her!—
You are to blame, my lord, to rate her so.

144 wrought: arranged

149 chop-logic: one who argues over fine points

151 minion: spoiled child

153 fettle your fine joints: prepare yourself

155 a hurdle: a heavy cart upon which criminals were taken to their execution
156 green-sickness carrion: anemic piece of flesh
157 tallow-face: pale-faced girl

159 but to: just let me

164 My fingers itch: I want to hit you.

168 hilding: the wretch
169 rate: scold

✳ **Would Therapy Help?**   Many critics believe that Lord and Lady Capulet have an unhappy marriage. Some productions of *Romeo and Juliet* have suggested this too. For example, in the movie versions of 1968 and 1996, Lady Capulet is seen flirting with Tybalt. What do you think of the Capulets' marriage, based on their behavior in the scene you are reading?

Lord Capulet rages at Juliet's disobedience.

The Nurse tries to intercede for Juliet, but Lord Capulet tells her to be quiet. He demands that Juliet obey him or be thrown out of his house.

CAPULET. And why, my lady wisdom? hold your tongue,   170
  Good prudence; smatter with your gossips, go.

NURSE. I speak no treason.

CAPULET.   O, God ye good-en!

NURSE. May not one speak?

CAPULET.   Peace, you mumbling fool!
  Utter your gravity o'er a gossip's bowl,
  For here we need it not.   175

LADY CAPULET. You are too hot.

✱ **CAPULET.** God's bread! it makes me mad:
  Day, night, hour, time, tide, work, play,
  Alone, in company, still my care hath been
  To have her match'd, and having now provided   180
  A gentleman of noble parentage,
  Of fair demesnes, youthful, and nobly train'd,
  Stuff'd, as they say, with honourable parts,
  Proportion'd as one's heart would wish a man,—
  And then to have a wretched puling fool,   185
  A whining mammet, in her fortune's tender,
  To answer, 'I'll not wed,—I cannot love,
  I am too young,—I pray you pardon me:'—
  But, an you will not wed, I'll pardon you:
  Graze where you will, you shall not house with me: 190
  Look to't, think on't, I do not use to jest.
  Thursday is near; lay hand on heart, advise:
  An you be mine, I'll give you to my friend;
  An you be not, hang, beg, starve, die i' the streets,
  For, by my soul, I'll ne'er acknowledge thee,   195

171 smatter: chatter—talk about things that you know nothing about

174 Utter your . . . bowl: Speak your important words to your gossipy friends.
176 hot: angry

177 God's bread: an oath on the wafer representing the body of Christ in the Holy Communion

181 parentage: birth
182 fair demesnes: beautiful estates
183 parts: characteristics, qualities

185 puling: whining
186 A whining mammet . . . tender: a crying doll, who when offered good fortune

190 graze: eat
191 I do not use to jest: I am not in the habit of joking
192 advise: think carefully on it

PERSONA JOURNAL

If you had overheard Lord Capulet's remarks to Juliet, would you have agreed with his position? Why or why not?

✱ **Censorship** Shakespeare wrote *Romeo and Juliet* during the reign of Queen Elizabeth, when playwrights could still use religious oaths like "God's bread!" But after Queen Elizabeth died and King James came to power, playwrights had to be more careful. In 1606, James passed a law forbidding playwrights to mention God at all—a law that Shakespeare obeyed in his later plays.

Lord Capulet leaves. Juliet pleads with her mother for help, but Lady Capulet also expresses her anger at Juliet and leaves. Juliet then seeks comfort from her Nurse. The Nurse, however, advises Juliet to forget Romeo and marry Paris.

        Nor what is mine shall never do thee good:
        Trust to't, bethink you, I'll not be forsworn.

[Exit.]

JULIET. Is there no pity sitting in the clouds,
        That sees into the bottom of my grief?
        O, sweet my mother, cast me not away!   200
        Delay this marriage for a month, a week;
        Or, if you do not, make the bridal bed
        In that dim monument where Tybalt lies.

LADY CAPULET. Talk not to me, for I'll not speak a word;
        Do as thou wilt, for I have done with thee.   205

[Exit.]

JULIET. O God!—O nurse! how shall this be prevented?
        My husband is on earth, my faith in heaven;
        How shall that faith return again to earth,
        Unless that husband send it me from heaven
        By leaving earth?—comfort me, counsel me.—   210
  ❋ Alack, alack, that heaven should practise stratagems
        Upon so soft a subject as myself!—
        What say'st thou? Hast thou not a word of joy?
        Some comfort, nurse.

NURSE.   Faith, here 'tis;
        Romeo is banished; and all the world to nothing   215
        That he dares ne'er come back to challenge you;
        Or if he do, it needs must be by stealth.
        Then, since the case so stands as now it doth,
        I think it best you married with the county.
        O, he's a lovely gentleman!   220

197 Trust to't: count on it

❓ Why does Juliet not tell her parents about her marriage to Romeo?

207 faith in heaven: the marriage ceremony

211 practise stratagems: play cruel tricks

214 Faith: indeed
215 all the world is nothing: the odds are
216 challenge: claim
217 needs must be by stealth: he will have to come in secret

❋ **Vocabulary Study** Juliet seems to have an extremely large vocabulary. Surely not many thirteen-year-olds have ever used words like "stratagems"—not even in Shakespeare's time. Shakespeare's own vocabulary was huge, perhaps the greatest of any author in history. He used about 30,000 words, some of which he made up himself.

Juliet is furious at the Nurse's suggestion that she forsake Romeo. She pretends to accept the Nurse's guidance and says she will go to Friar Lawrence for confession.

Romeo's a dishclout to him; an eagle, madam,
Hath not so green, so quick, so fair an eye
As Paris hath. Beshrew my very heart,
I think you are happy in this second match,
For it excels your first: or if it did not,   225
Your first is dead; or 'twere as good he were,
As living here, and you no use of him.

JULIET. Speakest thou this from thy heart?

NURSE. And from my soul too;
Or else beshrew them both.   230

JULIET. Amen!

NURSE. What?

JULIET. Well, thou hast comforted me marvellous much.
Go in; and tell my lady I am gone,
Having displeas'd my father, to Lawrence' cell,   235
To make confession and to be absolv'd.

NURSE. Marry, I will; and this is wisely done.

[Exit.]

JULIET. Ancient damnation! O most wicked fiend!
Is it more sin to wish me thus forsworn,
Or to dispraise my lord with that same tongue   240
Which she hath prais'd him with above compare
So many thousand times?—Go, counsellor;
Thou and my bosom henceforth shall be twain.—
I'll to the friar to know his remedy;
If all else fail, myself have power to die.   245

[Exit.]

221 a dishclout to him: a dishrag compared to him

223 Beshrew: curse

238 Ancient damnation! O most wicked fiend!: Damnable old woman! Most wicked devil!
239 forsworn: break my vow

243 bosom: real feelings; **twain:** separated

Friend or Enemy?   It is certainly shocking of the Nurse to suggest that Juliet marry Paris, and many readers and audiences have agreed with Juliet in calling the Nurse a "wicked fiend." But some scholars feel otherwise. For example, John C. Meagher insists that the Nurse ineptly "tries to make things best for her beloved Juliet," and that she doesn't deserve Juliet's burst of "self-willed fury." What do you think?

Reacting to Act III

Analysis

1. Why does Romeo first refuse to fight with Tybalt?

2. Whom do you think is to blame for the fight between Mercutio and Tybalt?

3. In your opinion, was Romeo justified in killing Tybalt? Why or why not?

4. Compare Romeo's reaction to his banishment with Juliet's response to the same news. Do these reactions reflect the way the characters have behaved thus far in the play? Why or why not?

5. The Friar says that Romeo, although banished, has many reasons to be grateful. List these reasons.

6. Review the Friar's plan on page 129. List each step of the plan in the left column of a chart like the one below. Next to each step, write things that could go wrong.

Steps in the Plan	What Could Go Wrong

7. What, if anything, prevents Juliet from simply joining Romeo in Mantua?

8. How have Lord Capulet's ideas about Juliet's choice of husband changed since Act I? Use examples from the play to support your answer.

9. Why do you think the Nurse advises Juliet to forget about Romeo and marry Paris? Does this advice surprise you?

Literary Elements

1. Why does Mercutio's speech "a plague o' both your houses" reflect one of the major **themes** of the play?

2. As you may recall, an **oxymoron** is a pair of words that seem to contradict each other, such as "heavy lightness." List the oxymorons you find on page 119.

Writing

1. What factor is most responsible for the difficulties facing the two lovers and their families? Write an essay that presents your opinion. Support this opinion with examples from the play.

2. Reread Act III, scene iv, noting the many references to time. Write a short essay explaining why you think Shakespeare chose to use this imagery and what effect it might have on the audience.

3. Summarize events in this act by writing one sentence that describes the events of each scene.

4. Assume you are a news anchor for a TV station. Write the story you would deliver about the tragic events that took place in scene i.

Romeo and Juliet

ACT IV

Claire Danes as Juliet
(Luhrman, 1996)

"Shall I be married then, to-morrow morning?"

Setting the Scene

ROMEO AND JULIET
Act IV, scene i *or* A Desperate Plan

Critical Query: To what lengths will Juliet go to avoid marrying Paris?

Time Capsule: Potions

At the end of this scene, Friar Lawrence will give Juliet a potion to put her in a deathlike sleep. Juliet is hardly the first fictional heroine to try this trick. In *An Ephesian Tale*, a Greek romance from the 2nd or 3rd century A.D., a heroine named Anthia takes a sleeping potion to escape an unwanted marriage. Shakespeare probably read that story. The Friar may have made his potion from a plant called a mandrake, which was sometimes used as an anesthetic.

Classroom Set Design

This is the basic Friar Lawrence cell design, with altar downstage left.

From the Prop Box

- Dagger for Juliet
- Vial for potion

Behind the Scene: Paris in the Hot Seat

This is the only time in the play when we see Juliet and Paris together, yet he's already addressing her as "my wife." Here's your chance to give Paris the third degree. What are his motives? How does he really feel about Juliet and the rest of the Capulets? What's his background? Does he think he'd make a good husband? When the scene ends, the actor who plays Paris must sit in the "hot seat" and answer questions from class members.

Warm-up Improv: What's the Plan?

If there's one thing you really don't want to do, it's_____. With a friend, brainstorm suggestions and come up with a plan that would help you avoid it.

Paris has come to Friar Lawrence to make arrangements for his marriage to Juliet. Paris explains that Lord Capulet is rushing the marriage because he believes it will help Juliet get over her grief for Tybalt's death. Juliet arrives to see the Friar.

ACT IV.

Scene i. Friar Lawrence's Cell

[Enter FRIAR LAWRENCE *and* PARIS.*]*

FRIAR. On Thursday, sir? the time is very short.

PARIS. My father Capulet will have it so;
    And I am nothing slow to slack his haste.

FRIAR. You say you do not know the lady's mind:
    Uneven is the course; I like it not.   5

PARIS. Immoderately she weeps for Tybalt's death,
    And therefore have I little talk'd of love;
✱   For Venus smiles not in a house of tears.
    Now, sir, her father counts it dangerous
    That she do give her sorrow so much sway;   10
    And, in his wisdom, hastes our marriage,
    To stop the inundation of her tears;
    Which, too much minded by herself alone,
    May be put from her by society:
    Now do you know the reason of this haste.   15

FRIAR. *[Aside.]* I would I knew not why it should be slow'd.—
    Look, sir, here comes the lady toward my cell.

[Enter JULIET.*]*

PARIS. Happily met, my lady and my wife!

JULIET. That 'may be', sir, when I may be a wife.

PARIS. That may be must be, love, on Thursday next.   20

2 father: prospective father-in-law

3 And I am . . . haste: I will not do anything to slow him down

6 Immoderately: excessively

10 That she do give . . . sway: That she allows her sorrow to overwhelm her
12 inundation: flood
13 minded . . . alone: which she thinks about too much when she's alone
14 May be . . . society: may be helped by having people around her

❓ Was Friar Lawrence being honest with Paris?

✱ **What's Your Sign?**   Astrology is the belief that the heavens influence human lives. There are many references to astrology in this play. For example, when Paris says that "Venus smiles not in a house of tears," he means the planet Venus as well as the goddess of love. And by "house," he means not only the Capulet's house, but a division of the sky called a "house." The astrological houses are symbolized by the twelve signs of the zodiac.

Juliet is caught off guard at the sight of Paris, but manages polite conversation with him. As with her mother earlier, Juliet says one thing but means another.

JULIET. What must be shall be.

FRIAR.   That's a certain text.

PARIS. Come you to make confession to this father?

JULIET. To answer that, I should confess to you.

PARIS. Do not deny to him that you love me.

JULIET. I will confess to you that I love him.   25

PARIS. So will ye, I am sure, that you love me.

JULIET. If I do so, it will be of more price,
Being spoke behind your back than to your face.

PARIS. Poor soul, thy face is much abus'd with tears.

JULIET. The tears have got small victory by that;   30
For it was bad enough before their spite.

PARIS. Thou wrong'st it more than tears with that report.

JULIET. That is no slander, sir, which is a truth;
And what I spake, I spake it to my face.

PARIS. Thy face is mine, and thou hast slander'd it.   35

JULIET. It may be so, for it is not mine own.—
Are you at leisure, holy father, now;
Or shall I come to you at evening mass?

FRIAR. My leisure serves me, pensive daughter, now.—
My lord, we must entreat the time alone.   40

PARIS. God shield I should disturb devotion!—
Juliet, on Thursday early will I rouse you:
Till then, adieu; and keep this holy kiss.

[Exit.]

? **25:** What does Juliet really mean by this line?

29 abus'd: injured

30–31 The tears . . . spite: The tears have made little difference, for my face was unattractive enough before I cried.
32 Thou wrong'st . . . report: You do more injustice to your face with that statement than those tears did.
34 spake: said

39 pensive: thoughtful
40 entreat: request

41 shield: forbid

? Was Juliet lying to Paris at any time?

PERSONA JOURNAL

Since you know both young men, whom do you think would make a better husband—Romeo or Paris?

⭐ **Stichomythia**   Note that much of the dialogue between Paris and Juliet in this scene consists of quick, single lines. This technique is called *stichomythia*, and it dates back to ancient Greek and Roman drama. Shakespeare used it frequently in his plays, often to witty effect. Here, it helps convey the tension and awkwardness between Paris and Juliet.

An unexpected meeting between Juliet and Paris
(Royal Shakespeare Company, 1961)

After Paris leaves, Juliet drops her composure, expresses anguish about her current situation, and threatens to kill herself unless the Friar can advise her on how to avoid marrying Paris. The Friar says he has thought of a possible plan.

JULIET. O, shut the door! and when thou hast done so,
Come weep with me; past hope, past cure, past help! 45

FRIAR. Ah, Juliet, I already know thy grief;
It strains me past the compass of my wits:
I hear thou must, and nothing may prorogue it,
On Thursday next be married to this county.

JULIET. Tell me not, friar, that thou hear'st of this, 50
Unless thou tell me how I may prevent it:
If, in thy wisdom, thou canst give no help,
Do thou but call my resolution wise,
✱ And with this knife I'll help it presently.
God join'd my heart and Romeo's, thou our hands; 55
And ere this hand, by thee to Romeo's seal'd,
Shall be the label to another deed,
Or my true heart with treacherous revolt
Turn to another, this shall slay them both:
Therefore, out of thy long-experienc'd time, 60
Give me some present counsel; or, behold,
'Twixt my extremes and me this bloody knife
Shall play the umpire; arbitrating that
Which the commission of thy years and art
Could to no issue of true honour bring. 65
Be not so long to speak; I long to die,
If what thou speak'st speak not of remedy.

FRIAR. Hold, daughter. I do spy a kind of hope,
Which craves as desperate an execution
As that is desperate which we would prevent. 70
If, rather than to marry County Paris
Thou hast the strength of will to slay thyself,

---

47 It strains me . . . wits: It exceeds the limits of my wisdom.
48 prorogue: postpone

54 I'll help it presently: I'll put my plan into action at once.

57 the label to another deed: the seal to another marriage

59 them both: my heart and hand

60–67 Therefore, from your many years of experience (**long-experience'd time**), give me some advice (**present counsel**). Otherwise, this knife will decide (**play the umpire**) whether my extreme difficulties (**extremes**) continue or I die, since all your authority (**commission**) and skill (**art**) could find no honorable solution.

❓ Do you think Juliet is really desperate enough to kill herself? Why or why not?
69–70 But it's as dangerous (**as desperate an execution**) as the danger we are trying to prevent.

✱ **Concealed Weapon**   A normally sheltered young woman like Juliet wouldn't have to wander far from home to meet danger in a Renaissance city—or at least in Shakespeare's London. So even women were armed whenever they left their houses. They carried small daggers called "bodkins" for self-protection.

The Friar begins to explain his idea. On Wednesday night, Juliet must drink a potion which will make it seem that she is dead.

Then is it likely thou wilt undertake
A thing like death to chide away this shame,
That cop'st with death himself to scape from it;   75
And, if thou dar'st, I'll give thee remedy.

JULIET. O, bid me leap, rather than marry Paris,
From off the battlements of yonder tower;
Or walk in thievish ways; or bid me lurk
Where serpents are; chain me with roaring bears;   80
Or shut me nightly in a charnel-house,
O'er-cover'd quite with dead men's rattling bones,
With reeky shanks and yellow chapless skulls;
Or bid me go into a new-made grave,
And hide me with a dead man in his shroud;   85
Things that, to hear them told, have made me tremble;
And I will do it without fear or doubt,
To live an unstain'd wife to my sweet love.

✱ FRIAR. Hold, then; go home, be merry, give consent   *Turning point*
To marry Paris: Wednesday is to-morrow;   90
To-morrow night look that thou lie alone,
Let not thy nurse lie with thee in thy chamber: *things won't go well*
Take thou this vial, being then in bed,
And this distilled liquor drink thou off:
When, presently, through all thy veins shall run   95
A cold and drowsy humour; for no pulse
Shall keep his native progress, but surcease:
No warmth, no breath, shall testify thou livest;
The roses in thy lips and cheeks shall fade
To paly ashes; thy eyes' windows fall,   100
Like death, when he shuts up the day of life;
Each part, depriv'd of supple government,

74 **chide away:** drive away

75 That requires you to deal (**cop'st**) with Death himself in order to escape (**scape**) this marriage.
76 **thou dar'st:** you have the courage

78 **battlements:** top

79 **in thievish ways:** on a road where thieves hide

81 **charnel-house:** vault where old bones are piled

83 with foul-smelling leg bones (**reeky shanks**) and yellow jawless (**chapless**) skulls

93 **vial:** small bottle

96 **drowsy humour:** sleep-inducing liquid
97 **surcease:** stop

102 Each part will be deprived of the ability to move (**supple government**).

✱ **The Best-Laid Plans**   In this speech, the Friar plots out a series of events leading to a happy ending for the lovers. Of course, you already know that *Romeo and Juliet* is a tragedy, so a happy ending isn't "in the cards." Can you predict some of the things that might go wrong with the Friar's well-meaning plans? Make your own estimate as you read the rest of the play.

Juliet will stay in a death-like state for forty-two hours. When she is found "dead," custom dictates that she will be placed in the Capulet burial vault. Romeo, alerted by the Friar, will arrive at the vault just before she wakes and take her away to Mantua. Juliet eagerly agrees to the plan.

Shall, stiff and stark and cold, appear like death:
And in this borrow'd likeness of shrunk death

✱ Thou shalt continue two-and-forty hours,   105
And then awake as from a pleasant sleep.
Now, when the bridegroom in the morning comes
To rouse thee from thy bed, there art thou dead:
Then,—as the manner of our country is,—
In thy best robes, uncover'd, on the bier,   110
Thou shalt be borne to that same ancient vault
Where all the kindred of the Capulets lie.
In the mean time, against thou shalt awake,
Shall Romeo by my letters know our drift;
And hither shall he come: and he and I   115
Will watch thy waking, and that very night
Shall Romeo bear thee hence to Mantua.
And this shall free thee from this present shame,
If no inconstant toy nor womanish fear
Abate thy valour in the acting it.   120

JULIET. Give me, give me! O, tell not me of fear!

FRIAR. Hold; get you gone, be strong and prosperous
In this resolve: I'll send a friar with speed
To Mantua, with my letters to thy lord.

JULIET. Love give me strength! and strength shall help afford.   125
Farewell, dear father.

[Exeunt.]

Juliet own her own actions (handwritten)

110 uncover'd: with an uncovered face; **bier:** a movable platform on which a corpse is placed before burial

113 against thou shalt awake: before you awake

114 drift: plan

119–120 If no fickle whim (**inconstant toy**) or womanish fears diminish your courage (**Abate thy valor**) to go through with it.

122 prosperous: successful

❓ What could go wrong with the Friar's plan?

✱ **". . . two-and-forty hours . . . "**   Juliet will sleep for forty-two hours, says the Friar. Some scholars think that his estimate is off and doesn't fit the action of the rest of the play. But they can't seem to agree as to whether Juliet needs to sleep longer or shorter than forty-two hours. One scholar has suggested fifty-two hours, another thirty-two.

Setting the Scene
ROMEO AND JULIET
Act IV, scenes ii and iii *or* Wedding Preparations

Critical Query: What contradictory moods are present in the Capulet household?

Classroom Set Design

This is the arrangement used in Act III, where the upstage right teacher's desk is a table in the first scene and Juliet's bed in the second. Aisles on either side of the seating will be used for entrances and exits.

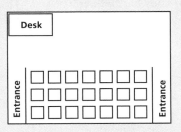

Time Capsule: Wedding Finery

In scene iii, Juliet and the Nurse go through her closet, choosing appropriate attire for her supposed wedding to Paris. Wealthy Italian women of the period usually wore three layers: First, a linen slip, next a garment of fine wool or silk, and finally an overdress which, for a wedding, would be covered with lavish embroidery and jewels. Hair was either elaborately dressed with coils and curls or covered with a jeweled or embroidered cap. To make them look taller, some women tweezed the hair on their forehead, to create a higher hairline.

Behind the Scene: Lady Capulet in the Hot Seat

Throughout the play, Lady Capulet's cryptic speeches make her a character open to several different interpretations. Here is your chance to discover how she really feels about her life and the other characters in the play. After scene iii ends, the actor who plays Lady Capulet must sit in the "hot seat" and answer questions by class members.

From the Prop Box

- Lord Capulet's guest list
- Dagger
- Vial for potion

Warm-up Improv: Tough Choice

You are ill and your only chance is a medicine that will either cure you or end your life. Through mime and monologue, show what you would do and say as you decide whether or not to take the medicine.

The Capulet household is busy preparing for the upcoming wedding. Juliet arrives, greets her father, and pretends to beg his forgiveness for her earlier disobedience.

Scene ii. Hall in Capulet's House

[Enter CAPULET, LADY CAPULET, NURSE, *and* SERVANTS.*]*

CAPULET. So many guests invite as here are writ.—

[Exit first SERVANT.*]*

✱ Sirrah, go hire me twenty cunning cooks.

2 SERVANT. You shall have none ill, sir; for I'll try if they can lick their fingers.

CAPULET. How canst thou try them so?   5

2 SERVANT. Marry, sir, 'tis an ill cook that cannot lick his own fingers: therefore he that cannot lick his fingers goes not with me.

CAPULET. Go, begone.—*[Exit second* SERVANT.*]*
We shall be much unfurnish'd for this time.—   10
What, is my daughter gone to Friar Lawrence?

NURSE. Ay, forsooth.

CAPULET. Well, he may chance to do some good on her:
A peevish self-will'd harlotry it is.

NURSE. See where she comes from shrift with merry look.   15

[Enter JULIET.*]*

CAPULET. How now, my headstrong! where have you been gadding?

JULIET. Where I have learn'd me to repent the sin
Of disobedient opposition
To you and your behests; and am enjoin'd
By holy Lawrence to fall prostrate here,   20
To beg your pardon:—pardon, I beseech you!
Henceforward I am ever rul'd by you.

---

2 cunning: skillful

3 none ill: none that aren't good; **try:** test

6–7 It's a poor cook who won't eat his own cooking.

10 We are not prepared (**much unfurnish'd**) for this wedding celebration.

13–14 Well, he may be able to do some good with her; she's a silly (**peevish**) good-for-nothing (**harlotry**).

16 gadding: wandering

❓ Why is Juliet not being truthful here?

19 behests: orders; **enjoin'd:** instructed
20 prostrate: face down

✱ **". . . hire me twenty cunning cooks."**   Do you remember when Capulet suggested a very small wedding for Paris and Juliet? "A friend or two," he said in III, iv. Of course, the wedding grew slightly larger only a handful of lines later: "Therefore we'll have some half a dozen friends . . ." Now he seems to be preparing for as many guests as he invited to his masked ball. Capulet is an impulsive character and doesn't mind contradicting himself.

Juliet declares that after meeting with Friar Lawrence, she is prepared for the wedding to take place. Lord Capulet is overjoyed by his daughter's change of heart.

CAPULET. Send for the county; go tell him of this:
I'll have this knot knit up to-morrow morning.

JULIET. I met the youthful lord at Lawrence' cell;   25
And gave him what becomèd love I might,
Not stepping o'er the bounds of modesty.

CAPULET. Why, I am glad on't; this is well,—stand up,—
This is as't should be.—Let me see the county;
Ay, marry, go, I say, and fetch him hither.—   30
Now, afore God, this reverend holy friar,
All our whole city is much bound to him.

JULIET. Nurse, will you go with me into my closet,
To help me sort such needful ornaments
As you think fit to furnish me to-morrow?   35

LADY CAPULET. No, not till Thursday; there is time enough.

CAPULET. Go, nurse, go with her.—We'll to church to-morrow.

[Exeunt JULIET *and* NURSE.*]*

LADY CAPULET. We shall be short in our provision:
✳ 'Tis now near night.

CAPULET.   Tush, I will stir about,
And all things shall be well, I warrant thee, wife: 40
Go thou to Juliet, help to deck up her;
I'll not to bed to-night;—let me alone;
I'll play the housewife for this once.—What, ho!—
They are all forth: well, I will walk myself
To County Paris, to prepare him up   45
Against to-morrow: my heart is wondrous light
Since this same wayward girl is so reclaim'd.

[Exeunt.]

24 **knot knit up:** marriage completed

26 **becomed:** proper

28 **on't:** of it

32 **bound:** indebted

33 **closet:** room

35 **to furnish me:** for me to wear

38 **provision:** supplies (food and drink)

39 **Tush:** Nonsense

41 **deck:** dress

❓ Lord Capulet is taking on duties that women of this period performed. How do you think Lady Capulet and the rest of the household react to this?
47 **this wayward . . . reclaimed:** this disobedient girl has come to her senses

PERSONA JOURNAL

Assume your character is involved with the wedding. How has this change of date affected you?

✳ **"'Tis now near night."**   Consider what has happened since this morning. Immediately after Romeo fled to Mantua, Juliet heard herself engaged to Paris; she hurried to visit the Friar where she spent no more than a couple of hours; then she came promptly home in time to take part in this scene. Realistically, only a few hours have passed—and yet Lady Capulet says, "'Tis now near night." Shakespeare has taken a few hours and made us believe a whole day has passed.

The Nurse and Lady Capulet offer to help Juliet choose her wedding attire. She politely sends them away and then, reflecting on what she is about to do, becomes fearful about taking the potion.

Scene iii. Juliet's Chamber

[Enter JULIET *and* NURSE.*]*

JULIET. Ay, those attires are best:—but, gentle nurse,
    I pray thee, leave me to myself to-night;
    For I have need of many orisons
    To move the heavens to smile upon my state,
    Which, well thou know'st, is cross and full of sin.   5

[Enter LADY CAPULET.*]*

LADY CAPULET. What, are you busy, ho? need you my help?

JULIET. No, madam; we have cull'd such necessaries
    As are behoveful for our state to-morrow:
    So please you, let me now be left alone,
    And let the nurse this night sit up with you;   10
    For I am sure you have your hands full all
    In this so sudden business.

LADY CAPULET.   Good night:
  ✱ Get thee to bed, and rest; for thou hast need.

[Exeunt LADY CAPULET *and* NURSE.*]*

JULIET. Farewell!—God knows when we shall meet again.
    I have a faint cold fear thrills through my veins   15
    That almost freezes up the heat of life:
    I'll call them back again to comfort me;—
    Nurse!—What should she do here?
    My dismal scene I needs must act alone.—
    Come, vial.—   20
    What if this mixture do not work at all?

1 attires: clothes

3 orisons: prayers

5 cross: perverse

7 cull'd: selected
8 behoveful for our state: appropriate for the wedding ceremony

15 thrills: running

19 dismal: dreadful

✱ **Bed? What Bed?** Since there was little realistic scenery in an Elizabethan theater, where was Juliet's bed in the original production? Some scholars suggest that a bed was temporarily brought on stage. Another possibility is that Juliet's bed was revealed in a curtained area at the back of the stage. The curtain could have been closed during scene iv, then reopened when the Nurse discovers Juliet's seemingly lifeless body in scene v.

Juliet considers all of the possibilities for error in the Friar's plan.

Shall I be married, then, to-morrow morning?—
No, No!—this shall forbid it:—lie thou there.—

[*Laying down her dagger.*]

What if it be a poison, which the friar
Subtly hath minister'd to have me dead,   25
Lest in this marriage he should be dishonour'd,
Because he married me before to Romeo?
I fear it is: and yet methinks it should not,
For he hath still been tried a holy man.
How if, when I am laid into the tomb,   30
I wake before the time that Romeo
Come to redeem me? There's a fearful point!
Shall I not then be stifled in the vault,
To whose foul mouth no healthsome air breathes in,
And there die strangled ere my Romeo comes?   35
Or, if I live, is it not very like
The horrible conceit of death and night,
Together with the terror of the place,—
As in a vault, an ancient receptacle,
Where, for this many hundred years, the bones   40
Of all my buried ancestors are pack'd;
Where bloody Tybalt, yet but green in earth,
Lies festering in his shroud; where, as they say,
At some hours in the night spirits resort;—
Alack, alack, is it not like that I,   45
So early waking,—what with loathsome smells,
And shrieks like mandrakes torn out of the earth,
That living mortals, hearing them, run mad;—
O, if I wake, shall I not be distraught,
Environèd with all these hideous fears,   50

25 minister'd: given

29 still been tried: always shown himself to be

? Why does Juliet think the Friar might have given her poison?

33 stifled: smothered

36 like: likely
37 conceit: idea

42 yet but green in earth: so recently buried
43 festering in his shroud: rotting in his burial cloth
44 resort: live

47 mandrakes: The root of the mandrake was said to have a human-like form, and it was reported that the mandrake screamed horrible cries when its roots were pulled out of the ground, driving listeners mad.
50 environed: surrounded

? What emotions might be running through Juliet's mind as she prepares to drink the potion?

* **Magical Mandrake** For centuries, the mandrake root was believed to have magical powers. It was used to make love potions, anesthetics, and healing balms. It was even thought to bring wealth, and its power to cure infertility is mentioned in the Bible (Genesis 30:14–16). It was often mentioned in poetry, including the first two lines of a poem by Shakespeare's contemporary John Donne: "Go and catch a falling star, / Get with child a mandrake root . . . "

And madly play with my forefathers' joints?
And pluck the mangled Tybalt from his shroud?
And, in this rage, with some great kinsman's bone,
As with a club, dash out my desperate brains?—
O, look! methinks I see my cousin's ghost   55
Seeking out Romeo, that did spit his body
Upon a rapier's point:—stay, Tybalt, stay!—
✳ Romeo, I come! this do I drink to thee.

[Throws herself on the bed.]

56 spit: pierce

57 stay: stop

Juliet prepares to drink the
potion. (Zeffirelli, 1968)

Juliet Drinks the Potion   Juliet's speech is one
of mounting horror, with one gruesome image
piled on top of another. At the end of it comes the most ghastly image of all—Tybalt's ghost seeking out
Romeo. At that moment, Juliet drinks the potion, when her fears are at their very height. How realistic do
you think this moment is? What effect do you think it would have on an audience?

Setting the Scene

ROMEO AND JULIET
Act IV, scenes iv and v *or* A Feast Becomes a Funeral

Critical Query: Who seems most upset by Juliet's death? Who seems least upset?

Classroom Set Design

Use the set-up from the previous two scenes but move teacher's desk slightly downstage for scene v so that some actors will be able to be on the upstage side of Juliet's bed.

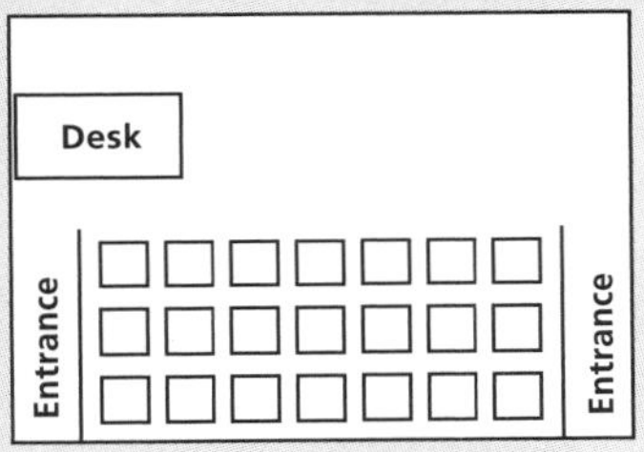

[Diagram: Desk at top, rows of seats with Entrance on left and right sides]

Special Effects: Musicians Approach

Near the end of scene iv, music offstage indicates that Count Paris is coming with musicians to gather Juliet and the Capulets and escort them to the church. If possible, play a recording of Renaissance music at this point, starting quietly and then increasing in volume as the musicians get closer to the Capulet household.

Warm-up Improv: Devastation

You and friends were playing ball when the skies darkened, and you ran for cover just before a tornado touched down. The winds have subsided; you have emerged from your hiding place and are the first people to observe the destruction.

From the Prop Box

- A set of keys
- Spits (used to roast the meat on; these might be nothing more than sticks)
- Logs (real logs or anything vaguely log-shaped can be used)
- Baskets (can be filled with cooking supplies)
- Instruments for musicians
- Dagger for Peter

Time Capsule: Musical Interlude

You'll soon meet a group of musicians. Music was everywhere in Renaissance Italy—in royal courts, churches, private homes, and even in the streets. Every gentleman was expected to be able to read music, play an instrument, and sing. The lute—a small, plucked, stringed instrument—was especially popular.

Scene iv. Hall in Capulet's House

[Enter LADY CAPULET *and* NURSE.*]*

LADY CAPULET. Hold, take these keys and fetch more spices, nurse.

NURSE. They call for dates and quinces in the pastry.

[Enter CAPULET.*]*

✻ **CAPULET.** Come, stir, stir, stir! The second cock hath crow'd,
The curfew bell hath rung, 'tis three o'clock:—
Look to the bak'd meats, good Angelica;   5
Spare not for cost.

NURSE.   Go, you cot-quean, go,
Get you to bed; faith, you'll be sick to-morrow
For this night's watching.

CAPULET. No, not a whit: what! I have watch'd ere now
All night for lesser cause, and ne'er been sick.   10

LADY CAPULET. Ay, you have been a mouse-hunt in your time;
But I will watch you from such watching now.

[Exeunt LADY CAPULET *and* NURSE.*]*

CAPULET. A jealous-hood, a jealous-hood!

[Enter SERVANTS, *with spits, logs and baskets.]*

Now, fellow, what's there?

SERVANT. Things for the cook, sir; but I know not what.   15

CAPULET. Make haste, make haste. *[Exit* 1 SERVANT.*]*
                    —Sirrah, fetch drier logs:
Call Peter, he will show thee where they are.

2 pastry: place where pastry was made

4 curfew bell: bell announcing daylight

6 cot-quean: man who does a housewife's work

8 For this night's watching: because you stayed up all night

❓ How is Lord Capulet treated by Lady Capulet and the Nurse?
9 No, not a whit: No I won't, not a bit
11 mouse-hunt: one who runs after women

13 jealous-hood: jealous woman

✻ **Just a Matter of Time** In Shakespeare's time, the cock was said to crow three times during the night: once at midnight, once at 3:00 a.m., and an hour before daybreak. The curfew bell rang at night to command citizens to get off the streets, then again to announce the arrival of day.

While Lord Capulet manages the final preparations, Paris arrives with musicians. The Nurse goes to wake Juliet.

2 SERVANT. I have a head, sir, that will find out logs
    And never trouble Peter for the matter.

[Exit.]

CAPULET. Mass, and well said; a merry whoreson, ha!   20
    Thou shalt be logger-head. *[Exit 2 SERVANT.]*
                Good faith, 'tis day.
    The county will be here with music straight,
    For so he said he would:—I hear him near.

[Music within.]

    Nurse!—wife!—what, ho!—what, nurse, I say!

[Re-enter Nurse.]

    Go, waken Juliet; go and trim her up;   25
    I'll go and chat with Paris:—hie, make haste,
    Make haste; the bridegroom he is come already:
    Make haste, I say.

[Exeunt.]

20–21 By the mass (**Mass—a mild oath**), that's clever. You are a happy rascal (**a merry whoreson**). You're a blockhead (**logger-head**). Good Heavens (**Good faith**), day has dawned (**'tis day**).

25 trim her up: help her get dressed
26 hie: hurry

❓ Considering the short time for the wedding preparations, many people in the Capulet house did not get much sleep last night. How do you think this will impact their reactions to Juliet's "death"?

The Nurse enters Juliet's chamber and tries to rouse her. When she realizes Juliet is dead, she screams for help.

Scene v. Juliet's Chamber

[Enter NURSE.*]*

NURSE. Mistress!—what, mistress!—Juliet!—Fast, I warrant her,
    she:—
    Why, lamb!—why, lady!—fie, you slug-abed!—
    Why, love, I say!—madam! sweetheart!—why, bride!—
    What, not a word?—you take your pennyworths now;   5
    Sleep for a week; for the next night, I warrant,
✱   The County Paris hath set up his rest
    That you shall rest but little.—God forgive me!
    Marry, and amen, how sound is she asleep!
    I needs must wake her.—Madam, madam, madam!—
    Ay, let the county take you in your bed;   10
    He'll fright you up, i' faith.—Will it not be?
    What, dress'd! and in your clothes! and down again!
    I must needs wake you.—lady! lady! lady!—
    Alas, alas!—Help, help! My lady's dead!—   15
    O, well-a-day that ever I was born!—
    Some *aqua-vitae*, ho!—my lord! my lady!

[Enter LADY CAPULET.*]*

LADY CAPULET. What noise is here?

NURSE.   O lamentable day!

LADY CAPULET. What is the matter?

NURSE.   Look, look! O heavy day!

LADY CAPULET. O me, O me!—my child, my only life!   20
    Revive, look up, or I will die with thee!—
    Help, help!—call help.

---

1 Fast, I warrant her: I'll bet she's fast asleep.

3 fie, you slug-abed: for shame, you sleepy head

5 your pennyworth's: little naps

7 hath set up his rest: is determined

12 fright you up, i' faith: frighten you awake, I guarantee

? It takes the Nurse about fourteen lines to realize that Juliet is "dead." What is the Nurse doing for the first few lines? When does she begin to realize that something is wrong?

16 well-a-day: alas the day
17 *aqua-vitae*: brandy

✱ **Multiple Meanings** Shakespeare often packed many meanings into few words, as when the Nurse tells Juliet that Paris has "set up his rest." "To set up one's rest" meant to stake everything at a game of cards. It also meant to make oneself at home or to be determined. After loading a musket, a soldier "rested" it on a pole before firing it. And during a jousting match, a knight "rested" his lance, or lowered it for a charge. "To set up one's rest" could also mean simply to relax.

Shocked, the Nurse and the Capulets gather at Juliet's bedside, grieving over her untimely death. Friar Lawrence and Paris arrive and join the mourning.

[Enter CAPULET.*]*

CAPULET. For shame, bring Juliet forth; her lord is come.

NURSE. She's dead, deceas'd, she's dead; alack the day!

LADY CAPULET. Alack the day, she's dead, she's dead, she's dead!   25

CAPULET. Ha! let me see her:—out alas! she's cold;
Her blood is settled, and her joints are stiff;
Life and these lips have long been separated:
Death lies on her like an untimely frost
Upon the sweetest flower of all the field.   30
Accursed time! unfortunate old man!

NURSE. O lamentable day!

LADY CAPULET.   O woeful time!

CAPULET. Death, that hath ta'en her hence to make me wail,
Ties up my tongue and will not let me speak.

[Enter FRIAR LAWRENCE *and* PARIS, *with* MUSICIANS.*]*

FRIAR. Come, is the bride ready to go to church?   35

CAPULET. Ready to go, but never to return:—
O son, the night before thy wedding day
Hath death lain with thy bride:—there she lies,
Flower as she was, deflowerèd by him.
Death is my son-in-law, death is my heir;   40
My daughter he hath wedded: I will die.
And leave him all; life, living, all is death's.

✳ **PARIS.** Have I thought long to see this morning's face,
And doth it give me such a sight as this?

39 deflowered: seduced

42 living: possessions

43 this morning's face: the morning of my wedding

✳ **Waiting in Vain**   "Have I thought long to see this morning's face, / And doth it give me such a sight as this?" asks Paris, as if he has been hoping to marry Juliet for a very long time. In fact, the possibility was first raised less than three days before. Shakespeare seems to be thinking of his source, Arthur Brooke's poem *Romeus and Juliet*, in which Paris waits a longer time to marry Juliet. "And now his longing heart thinks long for their appointed hour," writes Brooke, in a line that sounds strikingly like Shakespeare's.

The shock and mourning continue. Friar Lawrence, who knows that Juliet is not really dead, calls for calm and understanding.

LADY CAPULET. Accurs'd, unhappy, wretched, hateful day!   45
    Most miserable hour that e'er time saw
    In lasting labour of his pilgrimage!
    But one, poor one, one poor and loving child,
    But one thing to rejoice and solace in,
    And cruel death hath catch'd it from my sight!   50

✱ NURSE. O woe! O woeful, woeful, woeful day!
    Most lamentable day, most woeful day
    That ever, ever, I did yet behold!
    O day! O day! O day! O hateful day!
    Never was seen so black a day as this: 55
    O woeful day! O woeful day!

PARIS. Beguil'd, divorcèd, wrongèd, spited, slain!
    Most detestable death, by thee beguil'd,
    By cruel, cruel thee quite overthrown!—
    O love! O life!—not life, but love in death!   60

CAPULET. Despis'd, distressèd, hated, martyr'd, kill'd!—
    Uncomfortable time, why cam'st thou now
    To murder, murder our solemnity?—
    O child! O child!—my soul, and not my child!—
    Dead art thou, dead!—alack, my child is dead;   65
    And with my child my joys are buried!

FRIAR. Peace, ho, for shame! confusion's cure lives not
    In these confusions. Heaven and yourself
    Had part in this fair maid; now heaven hath all,
    And all the better is it for the maid: 70
    Your part in her you could not keep from death;
    But heaven keeps his part in eternal life.

47 In lasting . . . pilgrimage: in his long and difficult journey

49 solace in: take comfort in

50 catch'd it: snatched it

57 beguil'd: cheated; **spited:** wronged

59 By cruel, cruel . . . overthrown: You've cruelly destroyed her.

63 solemnity: festivities

❓ Each character on stage will express his or her grief differently. Choose one character and describe how that person would react to Juliet's death.

67–68 confusions . . . confusions: The cure for such ruin does not lie in such confused cries of grief.

✱ Serious or Soap Opera?   Do you get the impression that Shakespeare doesn't want us to take the grief of Paris, the Nurse, and the Capulets all that seriously? They don't express their sorrow in the play's greatest poetry. In fact, their language may even strike you as a bit ridiculous, full of melodrama and bombast (pretentiousness). Here Shakespeare seems to parody (make fun of) some of the lesser tragic writing of his time.

The Friar comforts the mourners and reminds them that Juliet has gone to heaven. Lord Capulet orders that the wedding preparations be converted to funeral plans.

The most you sought was her promotion;
For 'twas your heaven she should be advanc'd:
And weep ye now, seeing she is advanc'd   75
Above the clouds, as high as heaven itself?
O, in this love, you love your child so ill
That you run mad, seeing that she is well:
She's not well married that lives married long:
But she's best married that dies married young.   80
✱ Dry up your tears, and stick your rosemary
On this fair corse; and, as the custom is,
In all her best array bear her to church;
For though fond nature bids us all lament,
Yet nature's tears are reason's merriment.   85

CAPULET. All things that we ordainèd festival
Turn from their office to black funeral:
Our instruments to melancholy bells;
Our wedding cheer to a sad burial feast;
Our solemn hymns to sullen dirges change;   90
Our bridal flowers serve for a buried corse,
And all things change them to the contrary.

FRIAR. Sir, go you in,—and, madam, go with him;—
And go, Sir Paris;—every one prepare
To follow this fair corse unto her grave: 95
The heavens do lower upon you for some ill;
Move them no more by crossing their high will.

[*Exeunt* CAPULET, LADY CAPULET, PARIS, *and* FRIAR.]

1 MUSICIAN. Faith, we may put up our pipes and be gone.

73 her promotion: to see her well-married
74 advanc'd: raised

77–78 Do you love your child so little (**ill**) that you go into despair even when you know that she is better off?

85 Yet . . . merriment: Yet reason laughs at our natural grief because the dead are happier than we are.

❓ What does the Friar say to offer solace to the Capulets?
90 sullen dirges: mournful funeral songs

96 ill: sin (you have committed)

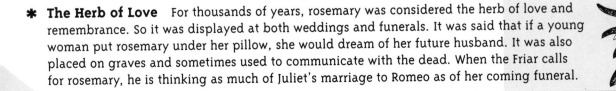

✱ **The Herb of Love** For thousands of years, rosemary was considered the herb of love and remembrance. So it was displayed at both weddings and funerals. It was said that if a young woman put rosemary under her pillow, she would dream of her future husband. It was also placed on graves and sometimes used to communicate with the dead. When the Friar calls for rosemary, he is thinking as much of Juliet's marriage to Romeo as of her coming funeral.

Peter asks that a comforting song be played. The musicians refuse, and a comic argument starts.

Act IV   Scene v

NURSE. Honest good fellows, ah, put up, put up;
For well you know this is a pitiful case.   100

[Exit.]

1 MUSICIAN. Ay, by my troth, the case may be amended.

[Enter PETER.*]*

PETER. Musicians, O, musicians, 'Heart's ease,' 'Heart's ease': O,
an you will have me live, play 'Heart's ease.'

1 MUSICIAN. Why 'Heart's ease'?

PETER. O, musicians, because my heart itself plays 'My heart is full   105
of woe': O, play me some merry dump to comfort me.

1 MUSICIAN. Not a dump we: 'tis no time to play now.

PETER. You will not then?

1 MUSICIAN. No.

PETER. I will then give it you soundly.   110

1 MUSICIAN. What will you give us?

PETER. No money, on my faith; but the gleek,—I will give you the
minstrel.

1 MUSICIAN. Then will I give you the serving-creature.

PETER. Then will I lay the serving-creature's dagger on your pate.   115
I will carry no crotchets: I'll *re* you, I'll *fa* you: do you note
me?

1 MUSICIAN. An you *re* us and *fa* us, you note us.

2 MUSICIAN. Pray you put up your dagger, and put out your wit.

100 case: situation (with a pun on instrument case)

101 amended: repaired

102 "Heart's ease": title of a popular song

106 dump: sad song

112–113 No money, I swear, but a mocking joke (**gleek**). I'll call you a two-bit musician (**give you the minstrel**).
114 Then I'll call you a lackey (**serving-creature**).
115 pate: head
116 I will carry no crotchets: I'll not put up with your whims—(besides meaning "whim," it is also a quarter note); **note:** understand (a pun on musical note)
119 put out: use

Music Music was very important in Elizabethan drama, and almost all of Shakespeare's plays include songs. A small orchestra of wind, string, and percussion instruments also played background or transitional music. At the end of a tragedy like *Romeo and Juliet*, several players performed a merry dance called a jig, led by the company's chief comedian. In *Romeo and Juliet*, this comedian was William Kempe, who played Peter. (See page 88.)

The musicians want to be paid before they play. An angry Peter leaves, but the musicians decide to stay for dinner.

PETER. Then have at you with my wit! I will dry-beat you with an   120
iron wit, and put up my iron dagger.—Answer me like men:

'When griping grief the heart doth wound,
And doleful dumps the mind oppress,
Then music with her silver sound'—

why 'silver sound'? why 'music with her silver sound'?—What   125
say you, Simon Catling?

1 MUSICIAN. Marry, sir, because silver hath a sweet sound.

PETER. Pretty!—What say you, Hugh Rebeck?

2 MUSICIAN. I say 'silver sound' because musicians sound for
silver.   130

PETER. Pretty too!—What say you, James Soundpost?

3 MUSICIAN. Faith, I know not what to say.

PETER. O, I cry you mercy; you are the singer: I will say for you. It
is 'music with her silver sound' because musicians have no
gold for sounding:—   135

'Then music with her silver sound
With speedy help doth lend redress.'

[Exit.]

1 MUSICIAN. What a pestilent knave is this same!

2 MUSICIAN. Hang him, Jack!—Come, we'll in here; tarry for the
mourners, and stay dinner.   140

[Exeunt.]

126–131 Peter is making fun of the musicians by making up last names for them that are also musically related, i.e., **catling:** catstring; **rebeck:** three-stringed fiddle; **soundpost:** wooden peg used to brace and support a violin.

133 cry you mercy: beg your pardon

137 redress: relief

138 pestilent knave: bothersome rascal

PERSONA JOURNAL

How does your character take the news of Juliet's death? How did you find out?

❓ Why do you think Shakespeare ended this scene with a light-hearted dialogue between Peter and the musicians?

No Laughing Matter Do you find yourself wondering why Shakespeare wrote a comical scene between Peter and the musicians at this particular moment in the play? Perhaps he didn't. One scholar has suggested that this scene was added by Thomas Nashe, a colleague of Shakespeare's. William Kempe, who played Peter, was the top comedian with Shakespeare's company. It's possible that he found his part too small and insisted on an extra scene to clown around in—so Nashe wrote it for him.

Reacting to Act IV

Analysis

1. Compare and contrast Romeo and Paris.

2. Why would Friar Lawrence ask Juliet to carry out a dangerous plan instead of just going to her parents and explaining that she was already married to Romeo?

3. What is your opinion of the Friar's plan? Use a chart like the one on page 146 to list the steps in the plan and suggest what might go wrong.

4. Lord Capulet moves up Juliet's wedding from Thursday to Wednesday. What effect might this have on Friar Lawrence's plan?

5. How has Juliet's relationship with her Nurse changed since the beginning of the play?

6. What differences are there among the reactions of Paris, the Nurse, Lord Capulet, and Lady Capulet to Juliet's "death"?

7. Which characters in this act do you have sympathy for?

Literary Elements

1. Shakespeare often adds humorous scenes to an otherwise serious play. These additions are known as **comic relief**. Where is this element found in Act IV? What purpose does it serve?

2. How many examples of **foreshadowing** can you find in this act?

Writing

1. Juliet has changed a great deal since the beginning of the play. Compose an essay explaining these changes. As a prewriting activity, complete a chart like the one below by writing three adjectives that describe her character in each of the first four acts.

Describing Juliet			
Act I	**Act II**	**Act III**	**Act IV**

2. Reread lines 18 through 43 in Act IV, scene i, and write down what Juliet might be thinking as she says these words to Paris.

3. Compose your version of Friar Lawrence's letter to Romeo telling him about Juliet's plans. Utilize the language of Shakespeare in writing the letter.

Romeo and Juliet

ACT V

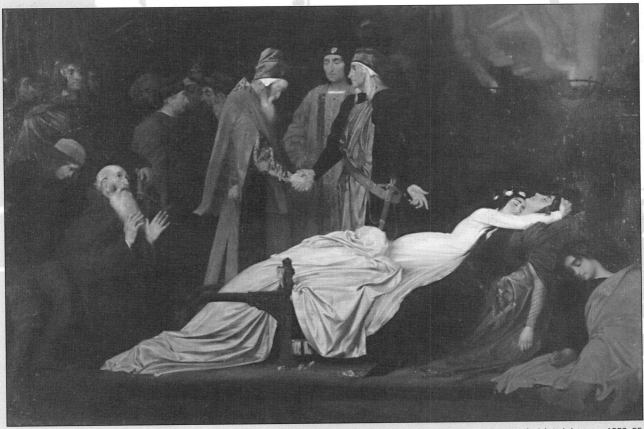

Reconciliation of the Montagues and the Capulets, Frederick Leighton, c. 1853–55

"For never was a story of more woe,
than this of Juliet and her Romeo."

Setting the Scene

ROMEO AND JULIET
Act V, scenes i and ii *or* The Plan Unravels

Critical Query: Was it fate that kept the Friar's letter from being delivered?

Classroom Set Design

Use the basic set-up for Friar Lawrence's cell with chairs or bench used as an altar. Acting area on stage right can become the street in Mantua for scene four.

Altar

Time Capsule: Poison Purchase

In the following scene, Romeo is able to buy poison quickly and easily. This would be no surprise in Renaissance Italy, where poisoning was something of an art. Even the great thinker and artist Leonardo Da Vinci (1452–1519) experimented at making better and more effective poisons. And members of the Borgia family, who held power in Italy during the 15th and 16th centuries, were rumored to have poisoned many of their enemies with a secret, deadly recipe.

From the Prop Box

- Coins
- Vial of poison
- Letter

Word Play: Dramatic Irony

You remember that dramatic irony occurs when the audience knows something that the characters on the stage do not. Given that we, the readers, already know from the Prologue that Romeo and Juliet die, what is ironic about Romeo's first speech in scene i?

Behind the Scene: Ye Olde Apothecary Shoppe

Despite the dire circumstances, Romeo takes time to describe the shop of a poor apothecary who provides a needed service. The apothecary, or pharmacy, of Renaissance Italy was a center for gossip and local news as well as a dispensary of herbs and medical advice. Most apothecaries were prosperous businessmen who served apprenticeships as youths and later joined guilds (labor unions).

Warm-up Improv: Homeward Bound

You are enjoying your vacation in Mexico with friends when a telegram arrives with news that forces you to abandon your trip and hurry home. Explain events to your friends and discuss them with others when you arrive at home.

As Romeo walks along a street in Mantua, Balthasar, his servant, arrives with news from Verona. Juliet is dead.

Act V.

Scene i. Mantua. A Street

[Enter ROMEO.*]*

ROMEO. If I may trust the flattering eye of sleep,
✱ My dreams presage some joyful news at hand;
  My bosom's lord sits lightly in his throne;
  And all this day an unaccustom'd spirit
  Lifts me above the ground with cheerful thoughts.   5
  I dreamt my lady came and found me dead,—
  Strange dream, that gives a dead man leave to think!—
  And breath'd such life with kisses in my lips,
  That I reviv'd, and was an emperor.
  Ah me! how sweet is love itself possess'd,   10
  When but love's shadows are so rich in joy!

[Enter BALTHASAR.*]*

  News from Verona!—How now, Balthasar?
  Dost thou not bring me letters from the friar?
  How doth my lady? Is my father well?
  How fares my Juliet? that I ask again;   15
  For nothing can be ill if she be well.

BALTHASAR. Then she is well, and nothing can be ill:
  Her body sleeps in Capel's monument,
  And her immortal part with angels lives.
  I saw her laid low in her kindred's vault,   20
  And presently took post to tell it you:
  O, pardon me for bringing these ill news,
  Since you did leave it for my office, sir.

---

2 presage: foretell
3 bosom's lord: heart
4 unaccustom'd: unusual

7 gives a dead man leave to think: allows a dead man to think

10 itself possessed: actually enjoyed
11 shadows: dreams

❓ What mood is Romeo in as this scene opens?

18 Capel's monument: Capulet's tomb
19 immortal part: soul
21 presently took post: immediately rode here
23 did leave it for my office: made it my duty

❓ How do you think Balthasar would speak the lines that give the news of Juliet's death to Romeo?

✱ **Irony** Act V of *Romeo and Juliet* is rich in irony, beginning with Romeo's opening soliloquy. He has had a dream which he believes is a prophecy of good fortune; actually, it is a prophecy of tragedy. As in his dream, Juliet will soon find Romeo dead—but she will not be able to revive him.

Distraught, Romeo makes plans to return to Verona and sends Balthasar to hire horses for the trip. After Balthasar leaves, Romeo resolves to join Juliet in death and makes plans to obtain poison for that purpose.

ROMEO. Is it even so? then I defy you, stars!—
    Thou know'st my lodging: get me ink and paper,   25
    And hire post-horses. I will hence to-night.

BALTHASAR. I do beseech you, sir, have patience:
    Your looks are pale and wild, and do import
    Some misadventure.

ROMEO.   Tush, thou art deceiv'd:
    Leave me, and do the thing I bid thee do.   30
    Hast thou no letters to me from the friar?

BALTHASAR. No, my good lord.

ROMEO.   No matter: get thee gone,
    And hire those horses; I'll be with thee straight.

[Exit BALTHASAR.*]*

    Well, Juliet, I will lie with thee to-night.
    Let's see for means;—O mischief, thou art swift   35
    To enter in the thoughts of desperate men!
    I do remember an apothecary,—
    And hereabouts he dwells,—which late I noted
    In tatter'd weeds, with overwhelming brows,
    Culling of simples; meagre were his looks,   40
    Sharp misery had worn him to the bones;
✱ And in his needy shop a tortoise hung,
    An alligator stuff'd, and other skins
    Of ill-shaped fishes; and about his shelves
    A beggarly account of empty boxes,   45
    Green earthen pots, bladders, and musty seeds,
    Remnants of packthread, and old cakes of roses,

24 then . . . stars: Romeo challenges the Fates, which have tried to keep him from Juliet.

❓ In one brief speech, Romeo reacts to the news of Juliet's death and decides what he will do next. If you were playing Romeo, how would you handle these lines?
26 hence: leave for there
28 import: suggest

35 Let's see for means: Let's see, what method shall I use?

37 apothecary: druggist
38 which late I noted: which I saw recently
39–40 In tatter'd . . . looks: In torn clothing (**weeds**), with overhanging eyebrows sorting (**culling**) medicinal herbs (**simples**); he was very thin.

45 beggarly account: small number
47 Remnants of . . . roses: bits of twine and old packets of rose petals

PERSONA JOURNAL

From what you know of Romeo, would you say that his quick decision to kill himself was in character? Why or why not?

✱ **Renaissance Drug Store** Romeo's description of the apothecary's shop is realistic. Renaissance apothecaries really did decorate their shops with weird items like stuffed alligators and tortoises. By "old cakes of roses," Romeo means cake-like objects made from pressed rose petals. These were used for perfume.

At an apothecary's shop, Romeo offers a great deal of money for some poison. The apothocary, however, says that the law prohibits selling poison on penalty of death. Romeo, noting the impoverished look of the man, argues that he should fear starving more than the law.

Were thinly scatter'd, to make up a show.
Noting this penury, to myself I said,
An if a man did need a poison now,   50
Whose sale is present death in Mantua,
Here lives a caitiff wretch would sell it him.
O, this same thought did but forerun my need;
And this same needy man must sell it me.
As I remember, this should be the house: 55
Being holiday, the beggar's shop is shut.—
What, ho! apothecary!

[Enter APOTHECARY.*]*

APOTHECARY.   Who calls so loud?

ROMEO. Come hither, man.—I see that thou art poor;
Hold, there is forty ducats: let me have
A dram of poison; such soon-speeding gear   60
As will disperse itself through all the veins
That the life-weary taker may fall dead;
And that the trunk may be discharg'd of breath
As violently as hasty powder fir'd
Doth hurry from the fatal cannon's womb.   65

APOTHECARY. Such mortal drugs I have; but Mantua's law
Is death to any he that utters them.

ROMEO. Art thou so bare and full of wretchedness
And fear'st to die? famine is in thy cheeks,
Need and oppression starveth in thine eyes,   70

49 penury: extreme poverty

51 is present death: means immediate death
52 caitiff: miserable

59 ducats: gold coins
60 dram: vial; **soon-spreading gear:** quick-acting substance

63 trunk: body
64 hasty powder fir'd: quick-firing gunpowder

66 mortal: deadly
67 he that utters them: person who distributes them

PERSONA JOURNAL

Describe the apothecary shop you go to in Verona. What do you buy there?

TALES FROM THE STAGE

Theatrical legend tells of an actor who fell on bad times and nearly starved. He became so thin and sickly-looking that he was cast as the Apothecary in *Romeo and Juliet*. He was a great success in the role and played it many times. However, success fattened him up and improved his health until he was no longer convincing as the impoverished druggist. He had to starve a good bit before taking up the role again.

The apothecary, unable to reject such a large sum, agrees to sell the poison, and Romeo sets off to Verona and Juliet.

Contempt and beggary hangs upon thy back,
The world is not thy friend, nor the world's law:
The world affords no law to make thee rich;
Then be not poor, but break it and take this.

APOTHECARY. My poverty, but not my will consents.   75

ROMEO. I pay thy poverty, and not thy will.

APOTHECARY. Put this in any liquid thing you will,
And drink it off; and, if you had the strength
Of twenty men, it would despatch you straight.

✳ **ROMEO.** There is thy gold; worse poison to men's souls,   80
Doing more murders in this loathsome world
Than these poor compounds that thou mayst not sell:
I sell thee poison; thou hast sold me none.
Farewell: buy food and get thyself in flesh.—
Come, cordial and not poison, go with me   85
To Juliet's grave; for there must I use thee.

[Exeunt.]

71 beggary: poverty

74 it: the law

79 despatch you straight: kill you immediately

❓ Paraphrase lines 81–84. What does Romeo say about gold?

84 get thyself in flesh: fatten yourself up
85 cordial: comforting drink that stimulates the heart

✳ **Money Is No Object**   Forty ducats was quite a lot of money in Shakespeare's time. In his early farce *The Comedy of Errors*, a character remarks that a diamond ring is worth forty ducats. But since Romeo is preparing to die, money is not important to him.

Friar John comes to Friar Lawrence to say that he has been unable to deliver the letter to Romeo that describes Juliet's artificial death. Friar Lawrence is concerned that Romeo may hear of Juliet's "death" without knowing that she is not truly dead.

Scene ii. Friar Lawrence's Cell

[*Enter* FRIAR JOHN.]

FRIAR JOHN. Holy Franciscan friar! brother, ho!

[*Enter* FRIAR LAWRENCE.]

FRIAR LAWRENCE. This same should be the voice of Friar John.
　　Welcome from Mantua: what says Romeo?
　　Or, if his mind be writ, give me his letter.

FRIAR JOHN. Going to find a barefoot brother out,　　　　5
　　One of our order, to associate me,
　　Here in this city visiting the sick,
　　And finding him, the searchers of the town,
　　Suspecting that we both were in a house
✱　Where the infectious pestilence did reign,　　　　10
　　Seal'd up the doors, and would not let us forth;
　　So that my speed to Mantua there was stay'd.

FRIAR LAWRENCE. Who bare my letter, then, to Romeo?

FRIAR JOHN. I could not send it,—here it is again,—
　　Nor get a messenger to bring it thee,　　　　15
　　So fearful were they of infection.

FRIAR LAWRENCE. Unhappy fortune! by my brotherhood,
　　The letter was not nice, but full of charge
　　Of dear import; and the neglecting it
　　May do much danger. Friar John, go hence;　　　　20
　　Get me an iron crow and bring it straight
　　Unto my cell.

4 his mind be writ: he wrote his thoughts
5 barefoot brother: Franciscans were instructed to walk barefoot and usually traveled in pairs.
5–12 I went to find another brother to accompany (**associate**) me to Mantua. He was visiting the sick, and the health officers (**searchers**) thought we had both been in a house filled with plague (**infectious pestilence**). They refused to let us travel (**seal'd up the doors**), so my trip (**speed**) to Mantua was stopped.

18–19 The letter was not trivial (**nice**), but full of news (**charge**) of great (**dear**) importance.

21 iron crow: crowbar

❓ What do you think the Friar is worried about?

✱ **". . . infectious pestilence . . . "** Friar John was quarantined for fear of the bubonic plague, a disease that may have killed more people than all the world's wars combined. Shakespeare himself survived several outbreaks, both in his hometown of Stratford and in the great city of London. During the Renaissance, no one knew that the plague was caused by fleas carried by rats. Far from preventing a spread of the disease, quarantines actually hastened more deaths.

Friar Lawrence decides to go to the Capulet vault to be there when Juliet wakes from the effects of the potion. He will then hide Juliet until Romeo can be contacted to come for her.

FRIAR JOHN.   Brother, I'll go and bring it thee.

[Exit.]

FRIAR LAWRENCE. Now must I to the monument alone;
    Within this three hours will fair Juliet wake:
    She will beshrew me much that Romeo   25
    Hath had no notice of these accidents;
    But I will write again to Mantua,
    And keep her at my cell till Romeo come;—
    Poor living corse, clos'd in a dead man's tomb!

[Exit.]

25 **beshrew:** blame
26 **accidents:** events

Setting the Scene
ROMEO AND JULIET
Act V, scene iii *or* A Somber End

Critical Query: How will this all conclude?

Classroom Set Design

Use standard Capulet/Montague divided seating. A row of chairs will divide the acting area, with stage right being the churchyard and stage left being the burial vault. The teacher's desk will be used as Juliet's bier.

Entrance

Church Yard

Desk

From the Prop Box

- Flowers for Paris
- Flashlights to use as torches
- 2 crowbars (or sticks)
- Broom or other implement to substitute for a mattock
- A letter
- A pouch of coins
- 2 swords or rapiers
- A vial of poison
- A lantern (or a flashlight inside a bag)
- A shovel
- A dagger

Time Capsule: Burying the Dead

The churchyard in the following scene is where Veronese commoners have been buried—but it's not like today's cemeteries. The ground is overcrowded with corpses, and no graves are marked. The air is filthy and unhealthy. The Capulets' tomb is probably a huge cellar underneath the church itself. Though decorated inside with sculptures or paintings, it is an even more awful place than the churchyard. Remember Juliet's remark that it has been packed for "many hundred years" with the bodies of her ancestors?

Warm-up Improv: Gone but not Forgotten

You're on Spring Break and you meet a wonderful person. Before you both leave for your respective homes, you plan to meet one last time for breakfast. But you oversleep and, panic-stricken, race to the place you were to meet—but he/she's gone! You search through your pockets for his/her home address and it's not there. What do you do now?

Paris arrives at the Capulet vault to leave flowers for Juliet. As he mourns, his page whistles to let him know someone is coming. Paris hides himself.

Scene iii. A Churchyard; with the Capulets' Tomb

[Enter PARIS, *and his* PAGE *bearing flowers and a torch.]*

PARIS. Give me thy torch, boy: hence, and stand aloof;—
    Yet put it out, for I would not be seen.
    Under yond yew tree lay thee all along,
    Holding thine ear close to the hollow ground;
    So shall no foot upon the churchyard tread,—   5
    Being loose, unfirm, with digging up of graves,—
    But thou shalt hear it: whistle then to me,
    As signal that thou hear'st something approach.
    Give me those flowers. Do as I bid thee, go.

PAGE. *[Aside.]* I am almost afraid to stand alone   10
    Here in the churchyard; yet I will adventure.

[Retires.]

PARIS. Sweet flower, with flowers thy bridal bed I strew:
    O woe! thy canopy is dust and stones!
    Which with sweet water nightly I will dew;
    Or, wanting that, with tears distill'd by moans: 15
    The obsequies that I for thee will keep,
    Nightly shall be to strew thy grave and weep.

[The PAGE *whistles.]*

    The boy gives warning something doth approach.
    What cursèd foot wanders this way to-night,
    To cross my obsequies and true love's rite?   20
    What, with a torch! muffle me, night, awhile.

[Retires.]

---

1 stand aloof: keep your distance

? Was Paris really in love with Juliet?

11 adventure: chance it

13 canopy: awning-like covering over a bed
14 sweet water: perfume; **dew:** moisten
15 wanting: lacking; **distill'd by moans:** created by my grief
16 obsequies: funeral ceremonies

20 cross: interfere with; **rite:** ritual
21 muffle: hide

? Are you surprised at the depth of Paris' grief? Why or why not?

✱ Elegy Throughout *Romeo and Juliet*, Shakespeare has been a bit of a poetic show-off, displaying his skill with various verse forms. These have included a serena, an aubade, and three sonnets. And now he gives us an *elegy* in Paris' six-line speech as he strews flowers on the tomb. An elegy is a sad poem, usually about departure or death.

Romeo arrives with tools to pry open the Capulet vault. He gives his servant Balthasar a letter to be delivered to Lord Montague, and commands his servant to leave. Balthasar pretends to go, but instead hides himself nearby.

[Enter ROMEO *and* BALTHASAR *with a torch, mattock, and a crow of iron.]*

ROMEO. Give me that mattock and the wrenching iron.
　　Hold, take this letter; early in the morning
　　See thou deliver it to my lord and father.
　　Give me the light; upon thy life I charge thee,　　　　25
　　Whate'er thou hear'st or seest, stand all aloof
　　And do not interrupt me in my course.
　　Why I descend into this bed of death
　　Is partly to behold my lady's face,
　　But chiefly to take thence from her dead finger　　　30
　　A precious ring,—a ring that I must use
　　In dear employment: therefore hence, be gone:—
　　But if thou, jealous, dost return to pry
　　In what I further shall intend to do,
　　By heaven, I will tear thee joint by joint,　　　　35
　　And strew this hungry churchyard with thy limbs:
　　The time and my intents are savage-wild;
　　More fierce and more inexorable far
　　Than empty tigers or the roaring sea.

BALTHASAR. I will be gone, sir, and not trouble you.　　40

ROMEO. So shalt thou show me friendship.—Take thou that:
　　Live, and be prosperous: and farewell, good fellow.

BALTHASAR. For all this same, I'll hide me hereabout:
　　His looks I fear, and his intents I doubt.

[Retires.]

22 Give me the pickaxe (**mattock**) and the crowbar (**wrenching iron**).

32 dear employment: important business
33 jealous: curious

38 inexorable far: relentless
39 empty: hungry

41 Take thou that: Romeo gives him money.

❓ Why does Balthasar contradict Romeo's orders and decide to stay and hide himself near the tomb?

181

Romeo begins to open the vault. Paris, knowing Romeo is a Montague, thinks he is there to desecrate Juliet's grave. He commands Romeo to stop. Romeo, in his impassioned state, tells Paris, whom Romeo does not recognize, to leave.

ROMEO. Thou detestable maw, thou womb of death, 45
    Gorg'd with the dearest morsel of the earth,
    Thus I enforce thy rotten jaws to open,

* *[Breaking open the door of the monument.]*

    And, in despite, I'll cram thee with more food!

PARIS. This is that banish'd haughty Montague
    That murder'd my love's cousin,—with which grief, 50
    It is supposed, the fair creature died,—
    And here is come to do some villanous shame
    To the dead bodies: I will apprehend him.—

[Advances.]

    Stop thy unhallow'd toil, vile Montague!
    Can vengeance be pursu'd further than death? 55
    Condemnèd villain, I do apprehend thee;
    Obey, and go with me; for thou must die.

ROMEO. I must indeed; and therefore came I hither.—
    Good gentle youth, tempt not a desperate man;
    Fly hence and leave me:—think upon these gone; 60
    Let them affright thee.—I beseech thee, youth,
    Put not another sin upon my head
    By urging me to fury: O, be gone!
    By heaven, I love thee better than myself;
    For I come hither arm'd against myself: 65
    Stay not, be gone;—live, and hereafter say,
    A madman's mercy bid thee run away.

PARIS. I do defy thy conjurations,
    And apprehend thee for a felon here.

---

45 maw: stomach (here, meaning the tomb)
46 Gorg'd with . . . earth: Filled with the sweetest thing on earth (Juliet)

48 in despite: with scorn

53 apprehend: arrest

54 unhallow'd toil: wicked work

❓ What emotions does Paris experience when he sees Romeo? How could an actor show this to the audience?

61 affright: frighten

❓ What does Romeo mean when he says, "I come arm'd against myself"?

68 conjurations: appeals

---

* Monument? What Monument? A stage direction calls for Romeo to open the monument. The scene then changes from the churchyard to inside the Capulet's tomb. Remember, realistic scenery was scarce in Shakespeare's theater. So how was this scene change done? Scholars believe that a small area at the back of the stage was concealed by a curtain. Romeo may have opened the curtain, revealing the bodies of Juliet and Tybalt.

Paris defies Romeo and challenges him to fight. He is fatally wounded and as he dies, asks to be placed in the vault next to Juliet. Romeo, now realizing who Paris is, prepares to honor his request.

ROMEO. Wilt thou provoke me? then have at thee, boy!   70

[They fight.]

PAGE. O lord, they fight! I will go call the watch.

[Exit.]

PARIS. O, I am slain! *[Falls.]* If thou be merciful,
    Open the tomb, lay me with Juliet.

[Dies.]

ROMEO. In faith, I will.—Let me peruse this face:—
    Mercutio's kinsman, noble County Paris!—   75
    What said my man, when my betossèd soul
    Did not attend him as we rode? I think
    He told me Paris should have married Juliet:
    Said he not so? or did I dream it so?
    Or am I mad, hearing him talk of Juliet,   80
    To think it was so?—O, give me thy hand,
    One writ with me in sour misfortune's book!
    I'll bury thee in a triumphant grave;—
 ✱ A grave? O, no, a lanthorn, slaught'red youth,
    For here lies Juliet, and her beauty makes   85
    This vault a feasting presence full of light.
    Death, lie thou there, by a dead man interr'd.

[Laying PARIS in the monument.]

    How oft when men are at the point of death
    Have they been merry! which their keepers call
    A lightning before death: O, how may I   90
    Call this a lightning?—O my love! my wife!
    Death, that hath suck'd the honey of thy breath,

---

71 the watch: the guards (During this time period, citizens patrolled the streets at night.)

74 peruse: look on

76 What did my servant say when my disturbed (**betossed**) soul did not pay close attention (**attend**) to him as we rode here?

82 We have both been written (**One writ with me**) about in sour misfortune's book.
83 triumphant: splendid

86 feasting presence: a room suitable for state banquets
87 Death . . . interr'd: Lie there, Paris (**Death**), you have been buried (**interr'd**) by someone who will soon be dead himself.

91 lightning: the lightening of the soul that is said to take place just before death.

✱ **"O, no, a lanthorn, slaught'red youth . . . "** By a *lanthorn* (or *lantern*), Romeo does not mean a hand-held lamp, but a tower with many windows brightly lit from inside. And when Romeo speaks of a "lightning before death," he refers to an old idea that people felt a sudden joy the moment before dying.

As Romeo lays Paris in the vault, he sees Juliet and Tybalt's bodies nearby. He asks Tybalt for forgiveness. As he gazes at Juliet, he marvels that her beauty has escaped the ravages of death. Romeo vows to stay with her for eternity and quickly drinks the poison.

Hath had no power yet upon thy beauty:
Thou art not conquer'd; beauty's ensign yet
Is crimson in thy lips and in thy cheeks,   95
And death's pale flag is not advancèd there.—
Tybalt, liest thou there in thy bloody sheet?
O, what more favour can I do to thee
Than with that hand that cut thy youth in twain
To sunder his that was thine enemy?   100
Forgive me, cousin!—Ah, dear Juliet,
Why art thou yet so fair? Shall I believe
That unsubstantial death is amorous;
And that the lean abhorrèd monster keeps
Thee here in dark to be his paramour?   105
For fear of that I still will stay with thee,
And never from this palace of dim night
Depart again: here, here will I remain
With worms that are thy chambermaids: O, here
Will I set up my everlasting rest;   110
And shake the yoke of inauspicious stars
From this world-wearied flesh.—Eyes, look your last!
Arms, take your last embrace! and, lips, O you
The doors of breath, seal with a righteous kiss
A dateless bargain to engrossing death!—   115
Come, bitter conduct, come, unsavoury guide!
Thou desperate pilot, now at once run on
The dashing rocks thy sea-sick weary bark!
Here's to my love! *[Drinks.]*—O true apothecary!
✱ Thy drugs are quick.—Thus with a kiss I die.   120

[Dies.]

94 ensign: banner

96 advanced: raised

(?) What is ironic about Romeo's description of Juliet's beauty?
99 twain: half
100 to sunder his: kill the one

103 unsubstantial: bodiless
104 abhorred: hateful
105 paramour: mistress
106 still: always

110 set up: take
111 yoke of inauspicious stars: grip of unkind fate

115 An eternal (**dateless**) bargain to all-consuming (**engrossing**) death.
116 conduct: poison
117–118 Romeo compares the poison and its effects on his body to a ship's captain (**pilot**) who destroys his boat (**bark**) by crashing it onto the rocks.

David Garrick

✱ **A New and Improved Ending?**   For about 200 years after his death, Shakespeare was considered a rather unskilled genius whose work needed revising. The actor/producer David Garrick (1717–1779) thought it a mistake that *Romeo and Juliet* didn't have a final love scene in the tomb. For his production of the play, he wrote more than fifty new lines in which Juliet awakened just after Romeo had taken the poison. The lovers had plenty of time to say farewell before Romeo died.

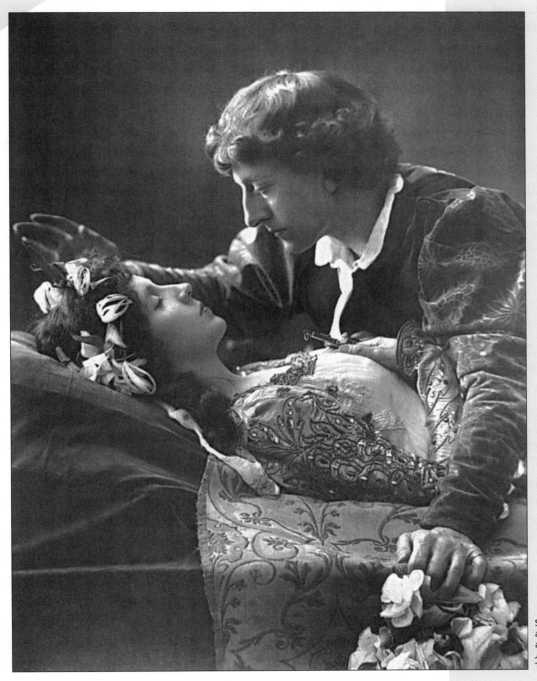

Sir Johnston Forbes-Robertson and Mrs. Patrick Campbell in a production of *Romeo and Juliet* at London's Lyceum Theatre, 1895

Friar Lawrence hurries to the graveyard, knowing that Juliet is due to wake soon. He sees Balthasar and asks why there is light coming from the Capulet vault. Balthasar says that Romeo has been in the vault for at least thirty minutes.

[Enter, at the other end of the Churchyard, Friar Lawrence, with a lantern, crow, and spade.]

FRIAR. Saint Francis be my speed! how oft to-night
　　Have my old feet stumbled at graves!—Who's there?

BALTHASAR. Here's one, a friend, and one that knows you well.

FRIAR. Bliss be upon you! Tell me, good my friend,
　　What torch is yond that vainly lends his light　　　　125
　　To grubs and eyeless skulls? as I discern,
　　It burneth in the Capels' monument.

BALTHASAR. It doth so, holy sir; and there's my master,
　　One that you love.

FRIAR. 　　　　　　　Who is it?

BALTHASAR. 　　　　　　　　　Romeo.

FRIAR. How long hath he been there?

✱ **BALTHASAR.** 　　　　　　　　　Full half an hour.　　　130

FRIAR. Go with me to the vault.

BALTHASAR. 　　　　　　　I dare not, sir;
　　My master knows not but I am gone hence;
　　And fearfully did menace me with death
　　If I did stay to look on his intents.

FRIAR. Stay then; I'll go alone:—fear comes upon me;　　135
　　O, much I fear some ill unlucky thing.

BALTHASAR. As I did sleep under this yew tree here,
　　I dreamt my master and another fought,
　　And that my master slew him.

121 **Saint Francis . . . speed:** (founder of the Franciscan order of monks) protect me.

✱ **All in Good Time**　When the Friar asks Balthasar how long Romeo has been in the tomb, Balthasar answers, "Full half an hour." Even though only a few minutes have really passed, an audience is likely to take Balthasar's word for it. As he does elsewhere in the play, Shakespeare skillfully manipulates our sense of time. The rest of the night will pass within minutes, and by the time the Prince delivers his final speech, it will be morning.

The Friar approaches the vault and sees blood near the entrance. Fearful, he enters and finds Romeo and Paris dead and Juliet beginning to wake. Juliet asks for Romeo, but the Friar, hearing a noise outside, urges her to leave the vault, telling her that Romeo is dead. The frightened Friar leaves, but Juliet refuses.

FRIAR.   Romeo! *[Advances.]*
    Alack, alack! what blood is this which stains   140
    The stony entrance of this sepulchre?—
    What mean these masterless and gory swords
    To lie discolour'd by this place of peace?

[Enters the monument.]

    Romeo! O, pale!—Who else? what, Paris too?
    And steep'd in blood?—Ah, what an unkind hour   145
    Is guilty of this lamentable chance?
    The lady stirs.

[JULIET wakes and stirs.]

JULIET. O comfortable friar! where is my lord?—
    I do remember well where I should be,
    And there I am:—where is my Romeo?   150

[Noise within.]

FRIAR. I hear some noise.—Lady, come from that nest
    Of death, contagion, and unnatural sleep:
    A greater power than we can contradict
    Hath thwarted our intents:—come, come away!
    Thy husband in thy bosom there lies dead;   155
    And Paris too:—come, I'll dispose of thee
    Among a sisterhood of holy nuns:
    Stay not to question, for the watch is coming.
✱ Come, go, good Juliet *[noise within]*,—I dare no longer stay.

JULIET. Go, get thee hence, for I will not away.—   160

[Exit FRIAR LAWRENCE.]

141 sepulchre: tomb

142 masterless and gory: abandoned and bloody

148 comfortable: comforting

152 contagion: contamination

❓ Do you think the Friar's frightened exit is in character? Why or why not?

✱ **Coward's Way Out** "I dare no longer stay," exclaims the Friar—then makes a hasty exit, leaving Juliet alone with Romeo's corpse. Scholars have often criticized Shakespeare's writing here, claiming that the Friar is too brave a character to abandon Juliet in such a cowardly way. And yet, Shakespeare had to get him offstage for Juliet's suicide.

Juliet kisses Romeo, hoping that some poison might still linger on his lips. When this fails, she takes his dagger and stabs herself. The night guards arrive, led by Paris' servant, and discover the bodies of Romeo, Juliet, and Paris.

What's here? a cup, clos'd in my true love's hand?
Poison, I see, hath been his timeless end:—
O churl! drink all, and left no friendly drop
To help me after?—I will kiss thy lips;
Haply some poison yet doth hang on them,   165
To make me die with a restorative.

[Kisses him.]

Thy lips are warm!

1 WATCH. *[Within.]* Lead, boy:—which way?

JULIET. Yea, noise?—Then I'll be brief.—O happy dagger!

[Snatching ROMEO'S *dagger.]*

✱ This is thy sheath *[stabs herself]*; there rust, and let me die.   170

[Falls on ROMEO'S *body and dies.]*

[Enter WATCH, *with the* PAGE *of Paris.]*

PAGE. This is the place; there, where the torch doth burn.

1 WATCH. The ground is bloody; search about the churchyard:
Go, some of you, whoe'er you find attach.

[Exeunt some of the WATCH.*]*

Pitiful sight! here lies the county slain;—
And Juliet bleeding; warm, and newly dead,   175
Who here hath lain this two days burièd.—
Go, tell the prince;—run to the Capulets,—
Raise up the Montagues,—some others search:—

[Exeunt others of the WATCH.*]*

162 timeless: untimely
163 churl: miser

165 Haply: perhaps
166 restorative: a healing medicine (here meaning Romeo's kiss)

169 O happy dagger: What luck—a dagger!

173 attach: arrest

PERSONA ACTION All men who are neither Capulets or Montagues arrive at the churchyard before line 171 as part of the Watch. Some leave at line 173; others at line 178.

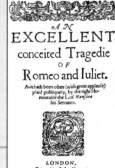

AN
EXCELLENT
conceited Tragedie
OF
Romeo and Iuliet.
As it hath been often (with great applause)
plaid publiquely, by the right Honourable the L. of Hunsdon
his Seruants.

LONDON,
Printed by Iohn Danter.
1597

✱ **Quartos and Folios** *Romeo and Juliet* was first printed in five pocket-sized editions called *quartos*. After Shakespeare's death, it was included in collections of his plays called *folios*. Shakespeare's original manuscripts don't exist, and none of the early editions of *Romeo and Juliet* are alike. So editors have to pick and choose among them for today's editions. For example, in most early editions, Juliet tells her dagger to "rest." But some editors prefer the word "rust," which appears in the first quarto.

Juliet kills herself with Romeo's dagger. (Zeffirelli, 1968)

The guards hold the Friar and Balthasar while they summon the Prince, the Capulets, and the Montagues. The Prince arrives and asks how and why the deaths have occurred.

We see the ground whereon these woes do lie;
But the true ground of all these piteous woes   180
We cannot without circumstance descry.

[Re-enter some of the WATCH *with* BALTHASAR.*]*

2 WATCH. Here's Romeo's man; we found him in the churchyard.

1 WATCH. Hold him in safety till the prince come hither.

[Re-enter others of the WATCH *with* FRIAR LAWRENCE.*]*

3 WATCH. Here is a friar, that trembles, sighs, and weeps:
We took this mattock and this spade from him   185
As he was coming from this churchyard side.

1 WATCH. A great suspicion: stay the friar too.

[Enter the PRINCE *and* ATTENDANTS.*]*

PRINCE. What misadventure is so early up,
That calls our person from our morning's rest?

[Enter CAPULET, LADY CAPULET, *and others.]*

CAPULET. What should it be, that they so shriek abroad?   190

LADY CAPULET. The people in the street cry Romeo,
Some Juliet, and some Paris; and all run,
With open outcry, toward our monument.

PRINCE. What fear is this which startles in our ears?

1 WATCH. Sovereign, here lies the County Paris slain;   195
And Romeo dead; and Juliet, dead before,
Warm and new kill'd.

PRINCE. Search, seek, and know how this foul murder comes.

179 woes: bodies of Romeo and Juliet
180 ground: cause
181 without . . . descry: understand without more details

PERSONA ACTION

Some of the Watch return with Balthasar at line 182; others enter at line 184 with Friar Lawrence.

187 This is very (**great**) suspicious. Keep (**stay**) the Friar too.

PERSONA ACTION

All Capulets and their households arrive at line 190.
188 What trouble (**misadventure**) has occurred so early in the day?

194 startles: causes alarm

195 Sovereign: Your Majesty

The Capulets grieve at the sight of Juliet's body. Lord Montague arrives.

Act V   Scene iii

1 WATCH. Here is a friar, and slaughter'd Romeo's man,
With instruments upon them fit to open   200
These dead men's tombs.

CAPULET. O heaven!—O wife, look how our daughter bleeds!
This dagger hath mista'en,—for, lo, his house
Is empty on the back of Montague,—
And it mis-sheathèd in my daughter's bosom!   205

LADY CAPULET. O me! this sight of death is as a bell
✱ That warns my old age to a sepulchre.

[Enter MONTAGUE *and others.]*

PRINCE. Come, Montague; for thou art early up,
To see thy son and heir more early down.

203 mista'en: mistaken; **his house:** the dagger's sheath

207 warns: summons

PERSONA ACTION

All Montagues, their households, and any other personas gradually fill the stage, beginning at line 208.

Phyllis Neilson-Terry and Vernon Steel

✱ **". . . That warns my old age to a sepulchre."**   In Act I, Shakespeare was very clear about Lady Capulet's age. Juliet is not yet fourteen, and Lady Capulet was even younger than that when her daughter was born. So Lady Capulet can't be more than twenty-six years old at the play's outset. But in the last scene, she seems ready to die of old age. As is often the case, Shakespeare is not a great stickler for consistency.

Lord Montague relates that his wife has died that night from grief over Romeo's banishment. He then sees Romeo's body. The Prince, determined to find out what has happened, questions the Friar.

MONTAGUE. Alas, my liege, my wife is dead to-night;   210
    Grief of my son's exile hath stopp'd her breath:
    What further woe conspires against mine age?

PRINCE. Look, and thou shalt see.

MONTAGUE. O thou untaught! what manners is in this,
    To press before thy father to a grave?   215

PRINCE. Seal up the mouth of outrage for a while,
    Till we can clear these ambiguities,
    And know their spring, their head, their true descent;
    And then will I be general of your woes,
    And lead you even to death: meantime forbear,   220
    And let mischance be slave to patience.—
    Bring forth the parties of suspicion.

FRIAR. I am the greatest, able to do least,
    Yet most suspected, as the time and place
    Doth make against me, of this direful murder;   225
    And here I stand, both to impeach and purge
    Myself condemnèd and myself excus'd.

PRINCE. Then say at once what thou dost know in this.

FRIAR. I will be brief, for my short date of breath
    Is not so long as is a tedious tale.   230
    Romeo, there dead, was husband to that Juliet;
    And she, there dead, that Romeo's faithful wife:
    I married them; and their stol'n marriage day
    Was Tybalt's doomsday, whose untimely death
    Banish'd the new-made bridegroom from this city;   235
    For whom, and not for Tybalt, Juliet pin'd.
    You, to remove that siege of grief from her,

---

210 liege: lord

214 untaught: ignorant boy

215 To press . . . grave: to die before your father

216 Seal up the . . . while: Stop this emotional outburst

217 ambiguities: strange events

219 general . . . woes: judge of your sorrows

220 forbear: no more

221 let mischance be slave to patience: bear your sorrows with patience

223–225 Because I was here tonight, I am the logical suspect for these terrible murders, even though I am too old and feeble to have done them.

226–227 both to impeach . . . excus'd: both to charge myself and clear myself, condemn myself and excuse myself

? Why does the Friar think he should be both condemned and forgiven?

229 short date of breath: time that I have left to live

233 stol'n: secret

234 doomsday: last day

236 pin'd: grieved

PERSONA ACTION

As you react to the Friar's explanation of events, remember to stay in character.

Betroth'd, and would have married her perforce,
To County Paris:—then comes she to me,
And with wild looks, bid me devise some means   240
To rid her from this second marriage,
Or in my cell there would she kill herself.
Then gave I her, so tutored by my art,
A sleeping potion; which so took effect
As I intended, for it wrought on her   245
The form of death: meantime I writ to Romeo
That he should hither come as this dire night,
To help to take her from her borrow'd grave,
Being the time the potion's force should cease.
But he which bore my letter, Friar John,   250
Was stay'd by accident; and yesternight
Return'd my letter back. Then all alone
At the prefixèd hour of her waking
Came I to take her from her kindred's vault;
Meaning to keep her closely at my cell   255
Till I conveniently could send to Romeo:
But when I came,—some minute ere the time
Of her awaking,—here untimely lay
The noble Paris and true Romeo dead.
She wakes; and I entreated her come forth   260
And bear this work of heaven with patience:
But then a noise did scare me from the tomb;
And she, too desperate, would not go with me,
But, as it seems, did violence on herself.
All this I know; and to the marriage   265
Her nurse is privy: and if ought in this
Miscarried by my fault, let my old life

238 perforce: by force

246 form: appearance
247 as: on
248 borrow'd: temporary
249 potion's force should cease: potion would wear off
251 yesternight: last night

253 prefixed hour: pre-established time
255 closely: secretly

266 is privy: knew about the secret marriage; **ought:** anything
267 miscarried: went wrong

PERSONA JOURNAL

What do you think the Capulets will do about the Nurse's involvement in these events?

As the Friar finishes his account, Balthasar gives the Prince the letter Romeo wrote to his father. The letter verifies what the Friar has said.

Be sacrific'd, some hour before his time,
Unto the rigour of severest law.

PRINCE. We still have known thee for a holy man.— 270
Where's Romeo's man? what can he say in this?

BALTHASAR. I brought my master news of Juliet's death;
And then in post he came from Mantua
To this same place, to this same monument.
This letter he early bid me give his father; 275
And threaten'd me with death, going in the vault,
If I departed not, and left him there.

PRINCE. Give me the letter,—I will look on it.—
Where is the county's page that rais'd the watch?—
Sirrah, what made your master in this place? 280

PAGE. He came with flowers to strew his lady's grave;
And bid me stand aloof, and so I did:
Anon comes one with light to ope the tomb;
And by-and-by my master drew on him;
And then I ran away to call the watch. 285

PRINCE. This letter doth make good the friar's words,
Their course of love, the tidings of her death:
And here he writes that he did buy a poison
Of a poor 'pothecary, and therewithal
Came to this vault to die, and lie with Juliet.— 290
Where be these enemies?—Capulet,—Montague,—
See what a scourge is laid upon your hate,
That heaven finds means to kill your joys with love!
And I, for winking at your discords too,
Have lost a brace of kinsmen:—all are punish'd. 295

269 rigour of severest law: harshness of the strictest law

273 in post: he quickly

279 rais'd: called
280 made: did

283 ope: open

286 make good: prove

289 therewithal: then

292 scourge: curse
293 your joys: your children
294 winking . . . discords: closing my eyes to your fighting
295 a brace of kinsmen: two relatives

Lords Capulet and Montague, seeing what their enmity has cost, agree to end their feud and build a golden monument in honor of their children.

CAPULET. O brother Montague, give me thy hand:
　　This is my daughter's jointure, for no more
　　Can I demand.

MONTAGUE. 　　　　But I can give thee more:
　　For I will raise her statue in pure gold;
　　That while Verona by that name is known,　　　　300
　　There shall no figure at such rate be set
　　As that of true and faithful Juliet.

CAPULET. As rich shall Romeo's by his lady's lie;
　　Poor sacrifices of our enmity!

PRINCE. A glooming peace this morning with it brings;　　305
✱　The sun for sorrow will not show his head.
　　Go hence, to have more talk of these sad things;
　　Some shall be pardon'd, and some punishèd;
　　For never was a story of more woe
　　Than this of Juliet and her Romeo.　　　　310

[Exeunt.]

297 jointure: dowry

301 at such rate be set: so highly valued

304 of our enmity: of our feud

305 glooming: melancholy

PERSONA JOURNAL

Do you believe that the feud is really over?

PERSONA JOURNAL

How do you think Verona will change because of these events?

✱ **"The sun for sorrow will not show his head."**　Do you remember when Juliet mentioned Phaeton at the beginning of Act III, scene ii? Phaeton died trying to drive the chariot of his father, the sun-god. Here at the end of *Romeo and Juliet*, Shakespeare refers again to the story of Phaeton. According to the Roman poet Ovid, the grieving sun-god refused to fly for a full day after Phaeton's death—just as the sorrowful sun will not shine after the deaths of Romeo and Juliet.

The funeral procession (Zeffirelli, 1968)

What Happens Afterward?   Shakespeare based the story of his play on *Romeus and Juliet*, a poem by Arthur Brooke. At the end of his poem, Brooke tells what happens to several characters after the lovers' deaths. For concealing the marriage from Lord and Lady Capulet, the Nurse is banished from Verona. For selling poison, the Apothecary is hanged. The Friar leaves Verona and becomes a hermit, dying five years later.

Reacting to Act V

Analysis

1. How does Romeo convince the Apothecary to sell him poison?

2. Explain why Father John fails to get Friar Lawrence's letter to Romeo.

3. Why do you think Balthasar ignores Romeo's threats and stays near the vault?

4. Why does Paris challenge Romeo in the churchyard?

5. Friar Lawrence runs from the tomb after Juliet awakens. Is this action "in character"? Why or why not?

6. Why do you think Shakespeare includes the deaths of Paris and Lady Montague in Act V?

7. What might Lords Capulet and Montague be thinking as they listen to the Friar's explanation of what has happened to their children?

8. Do you think that the feud between the Capulets and the Montagues is really over? Explain your answer.

Literary Elements

1. The **theme** of a work of literature is the message about life that the author wants to convey. A work as complex as a Shakespeare play will generally have more than one theme. With your classmates, discuss the theme(s) found in *Romeo and Juliet.*

2. The **climax** is the point in the plot where emotional tension is at its highest and where we know how the conflict will end. In Shakespeare's plays, the climax is usually in the last act. Where would you say the climax occurs in Act V?

Writing

1. Review the description of the apothecary's shop on pages 174–175, paying special attention to the descriptive adjectives. Now, write a description of the Capulet burial vault. Try imitating Shakespeare's style.

2. Using the Venn diagram that you completed after Act I (a comparison of your persona with a major character), write a short essay on the changes and growth of both your persona and the major character you selected. How did the events of the play affect both characters?

3. Compose your version of Romeo's letter to his father.

Reacting to the Play

Analysis

1. In your opinion, was the love between Romeo and Juliet deep and true, or were they just two immature adolescents who acted irrationally? Defend your position.

2. Select one of the three letters (Tybalt's challenge to Romeo, Friar Lawrence's explanation to Romeo, and Romeo's explanation to his father) and consider the possibility of how the play might have changed if any of the three letters had been delivered.

3. What if Romeo and Juliet had not died? What do you think their married life would have been like fifteen years later?

4. In small groups, examine the concept of cause and effect by creating a cause-effect chain beginning with Mercutio's death and continuing through the end of the play. A sample chain has been started below.

> **Tybalt kills Mercutio**
> *and so*
> **Romeo kills Tybalt**
> *and so*
> **Romeo is banished**
> *and so*

5. Identify some situations in today's world where two lovers might find obstacles because of their birthrights or beliefs.

6. Judging from the play, how do you think gender roles have changed since the Renaissance?

Literary Elements

A **tragedy** is a serious work of literature that narrates the events leading to the downfall of a **tragic hero**, who is usually of noble birth. His downfall is a result of a **tragic flaw** or fatal character weakness. For example, in Shakespeare's *Macbeth*, the hero's flaw is ambition. In *Othello*, it is jealousy. In your opinion, who is the hero (or heroine) of *Romeo and Juliet*? What is his/her tragic flaw?

Writing

1. In your opinion, which characters and/or events are responsible for the deaths of Romeo and Juliet? What role do you think fate plays? Explain your ideas in an expository essay.

2. Whom would you choose for a personal adviser—the Nurse, Juliet, Mercutio, or Friar Lawrence? Write an essay commenting on how that character influences others in the play and why his or her philosophy appeals to you.

3. Write a short parody of *Romeo and Juliet*.

4. Choose one scene from the play and rewrite the dialogue in modern English.

Life in Renaissance Italy

The Renaissance began in Italy. Although historians have many different opinions about *when* it began, somewhere around 1375 seems a pretty good date. The word *renaissance* means "rebirth." And indeed, at least some of the people who lived during that time thought that civilization itself was being reborn.

The Roman Empire had collapsed back in 476 A.D., marking an end to the civilizations of antiquity. For Europe, the thousand years that followed the fall of Rome is now commonly called the "Middle Ages." It is also sometimes called the "Dark Ages," because some people believe that the great learning of the ancient Greeks and Romans was forgotten during that time.

That's not quite true. There was plenty of learning during the Middle Ages—and plenty of great art, poetry, and philosophy. So the Middle Ages weren't nearly as "dark" as they're often made out to be. Nevertheless, only a very small number of people—clergymen, mostly—had access to education. Even kings and nobles were often illiterate. During the early days of the Italian Renaissance, much of that began to change.

Italy wasn't a nation back then. Instead, it was littered with independent and often warlike city-states. These included Florence, Venice, Ferrara, Rome—and of course, Verona, the scene of *Romeo and Juliet.*

As the Renaissance got under way, city-states grew larger and more powerful. More and more of their citizens became interested in literature, art, and science. Part of this increase in learning was due to printed books, which first arrived in Italy in 1465. For thousands of years, books had been hand-copied and were available only to a privileged few. Because of the printing press, many more people could buy books, and ideas began to spread.

But what was life like in the Italian Renaissance? It depended on who you were. The great majority of people were common laborers and peasants who lived in poverty. If you were one of them, the Renaissance wouldn't seem any different than the times before it. Life was short, hard, and painful. New developments in art and culture wouldn't have affected you a bit.

But if you were wealthy, that was another story. It also helped to be male. Women were generally thought of as the property of men, and marriage was considered a business deal. Although a few women gained power and education during the Renaissance, most did not.

So women had very little freedom. For example, you may have noticed that Juliet wasn't even allowed to leave the house unless she was on her way to confession! Young men like Romeo, Mercutio, and Tybalt could come and go as they liked. It was a great time for them.

Boys from well-off families went to school, and those from really rich families learned from private tutors. The right education was highly valued for a young gentleman. He was expected to become an extremely well-rounded individual. He had to excel in athletics, arts, letters, politics, and morals. More than that, he had to develop *nonchalance*—the appearance of doing all this effortlessly! This is what it meant to be a "Renaissance man."

As you might guess, the Renaissance was a time of intense individualism. This, too, made it different from the time that came before it. During the Middle Ages, the individual was not thought to be especially important. People generally considered themselves part of some group—usually a large, extended family.

As a result, there was little privacy during the Middle Ages. Even in wealthy families, several people slept in a single bed. But during the Italian Renaissance, privacy became more valued. A young girl like Juliet actually got to have her own bedroom!

This growth in individualism also affected eating habits. During the Middle Ages, meals were quite chaotic. A single tray was set in the middle of a table, and people grabbed whatever they could from it with their bare hands. They drank from a single cup passed from person to person. They didn't even have individual plates or table settings.

Today's eating utensils—plates, forks, spoons, knives, napkins, and drinking glasses—didn't appear until the Renaissance. When every person had his or her own place at the dinner table, even eating took on an individualistic air. This led to elaborate table etiquette, or manners.

In fact, etiquette became more important in almost all aspects of life, including the way people fought. The Renaissance was a quarrelsome age. When one city wasn't fighting another city, its citizens were fighting each other—just like the Montagues and Capulets. But even fighting had to be done properly. Like Mercutio and Tybalt, young men learned elaborate rules for fighting, whether in wars or duels.

It was an exciting time, at least for some. But don't get the idea that it was a glamorous one. Women of all classes often died in childbirth, and children just as often died in infancy. And if you became seriously ill in adulthood, you were likely not to survive. Although there were doctors aplenty, they were mostly quacks (fakes or pretenders). They had no way of learning anything about what we'd call medicine today. Out of ignorance, doctors killed more people than they healed.

Among diseases, the Black Death was the most dreaded. During the 1300s, this plague killed off perhaps a third of Europe's population. And it made numerous returns throughout the Renaissance, slaying both rich and poor in terrible numbers. Because nobody knew that the Black Death was initially spread by flea-carrying rats, nobody could do anything to stop it.

Simple cleanliness was another problem. People mistrusted water, so even the wealthy never really bathed. Of course, the well-to-do were concerned about appearances. So they kept their elegant, expensive clothes reasonably clean. They also tried to keep dirt off their hands and faces. But they did so by wiping themselves off, not by actually washing.

To put it bluntly, people were filthy and smelly. Because of poor dental hygiene, they also had bad teeth and bad breath. They tried to cover up their body odor with perfumes. They also used mints or candies for their breath—the "sweetmeats" Mercutio mentions in his Queen Mab speech (pp. 49–50).

In short, Renaissance Italy might make a great place to visit, but you wouldn't want to

live there. And sad to say, you probably wouldn't want to get very close to a real-life Romeo or Juliet.

Although historians disagree widely on when the Italian Renaissance ended, some say it was in the early 1500s. Italian culture didn't really lose its excitement after that. Many great books, artworks, and scientific discoveries were still in store. But how could a movement more than 150 years old continue to be called a "renaissance"—a rebirth? The Italian Renaissance got too old for its name.

But other countries picked up the torch, and pretty soon faraway England was in the midst of its own exciting Renaissance. Out of this came a great playwright named William Shakespeare, who wrote a play set in Renaissance Italy called *Romeo and Juliet.*

Shakespeare's Life

Many great authors can be imagined as living among the characters in their works. Historical records reveal how these writers spoke, felt, and thought. But Shakespeare is more mysterious. He never gave an interview or wrote an autobiography—not even one of his letters survives. What we know about his life can be told very briefly.

Shakespeare was born in April 1564. The exact date of his birth is unknown, but he was baptized on April 26 in the Stratford-upon-Avon church. His father, John, was a prominent local man who served as town chamberlain and mayor. Young William attended grammar school in Stratford, where he would have learned Latin—a requirement for a professional career—and some Greek.

Shakespeare's schoolroom

In 1582, William married Anne Hathaway. He was eighteen; she was twenty-six. At the time of their marriage, Anne was already three months pregnant with their first daughter, Susanna. In 1585, the couple had twins, Judith and Hamnet. Hamnet died before reaching adulthood, leaving Shakespeare no male heir.

Even less than usual is known about Shakespeare's life between 1585 and 1592. During that time, he moved to London and became an actor and playwright. He left his family behind in Stratford. Although he surely visited them occasionally, we have little evidence about what Shakespeare was like as a father and a husband.

Several of his early plays were written during this time, including *The Comedy of Errors, Titus Andronicus,* and the three parts of *Henry VI.* In those days, working in the theater was rather like acting in soap operas today—the results may be popular, but daytime serials aren't recognized as serious art. In fact, many people were opposed to even allowing plays to be performed. Ministers warned their congregations of the dangers of going to plays.

But Shakespeare and his friends were lucky. Queen Elizabeth I loved plays. She protected acting companies from restrictive laws and gave them her permission to perform.

Queen Elizabeth I

Shakespeare wrote several plays to be performed for the queen, including *Twelfth Night.*

After Elizabeth's death in 1603, Shakespeare's company became known as the King's Men. This group of actors performed for James I, who had ruled Scotland before becoming King of England. Perhaps to thank James for his patronage, Shakespeare wrote *Macbeth,* which included two topics of strong interest to the king—Scottish royalty and witchcraft.

Unlike many theater people, Shakespeare actually earned a good living. By 1599, he was part-owner of the Globe, one of the newest theaters in London. Such plays as *Othello, Hamlet,* and *King Lear* were first performed there.

In 1610 or 1611, Shakespeare moved back to the familiar surroundings of Stratford-upon-Avon. He was almost fifty years old, well past middle age by 17th-century standards. Over the years, he'd invested in property around Stratford, acquiring a comfortable estate and a family coat of arms.

But Shakespeare didn't give up writing. In 1611, his new play *The Tempest* was performed at Court. In 1613, his play *Henry VIII* premiered. This performance was more dramatic than anyone had expected. The stage directions called for a cannon to be fired when "King Henry" came on stage. The explosion set the stage on fire, and the entire theater burned to the ground.

Shakespeare died in 1616 at the age of fifty-two. Scholars have wondered why he willed his "second-best bed" to his widow, but he also left Anne his plays and a comfortable income. His gravestone carried this inscription:

> **Good friend for Jesus sake forbear**
> **To dig the dust enclosed here!**
> **Blest be the man that spares these stones,**
> **And curst be he that moves my bones.**

Shakespeare's Theatre

In Shakespeare's London, a day's entertainment often began with a favorite amusement, bearbaiting. A bear would be captured and chained to a stake inside a pit. A pack of dogs would be released, and they would attack the bear. Spectators placed bets on which would die first. Admission to these pits cost only a penny, so they were very popular with working-class Londoners.

After the bearbaiting was over, another penny purchased admission to a play. Each theater had its own company of actors, often supported by a nobleman or a member of the royal family.

As part-owner of the Globe Theatre, Shakespeare wrote plays, hired actors, and paid the bills. Since the Globe presented a new play every three weeks, Shakespeare and his actors had little time to rehearse or polish their productions. To complicate matters even more, most actors played more than one part in a play.

Boys played all the female roles. Most acting companies had three or four youths who were practically raised in the theater. They started acting as early as age seven and played female roles until they began shaving. Actresses would not become part of the English theater for another fifty years.

The audience crowded into the theater at about 2 p.m. The cheapest seats weren't seats at all but standing room in front of the stage. This area, known as the "pit," was occupied by "groundlings" or "penny knaves," who could be more trouble to the actors than they were worth. If the play was boring, the groundlings would throw rotten eggs or vegetables. They talked loudly to their friends, played cards, and even picked fights with each other. One theater was set on fire by audience members who didn't like the play.

The theater was open to the sky, so rain or snow presented a problem. However, the actors were partially protected by a roof known as the "heavens," and wealthier patrons sat in three stories of sheltered galleries that surrounded the pit and most of the main stage.

The main stage, about twenty-five feet deep and forty-five feet wide, projected into the audience, so spectators were closely involved in the action. This stage was rather

The Swan Theatre in London, drawn by Arend van Buchell in 1596.

bare, with only a few pieces of furniture. But this simplicity allowed for flexible and fluid staging. Unlike too many later productions, plays at the Globe did not grind to a halt for scene changes. When one group of actors exited through a doorway and a new group entered through another, Shakespeare's audience understood that a new location was probably being represented.

So the action of the plays was exciting and swift. The Chorus of *Romeo and Juliet* speaks of "the two hours' traffic of our stage," which suggests a rate of performance and delivery that today's actors would find nearly impossible.

Behind the main stage was the "tiring-house" where the actors changed costumes. Above the stage was a gallery that, when it wasn't occupied by musicians or wealthy patrons, could suggest any kind of high place—castle ramparts, a cliff, or a balcony. Although *Romeo and Juliet* was written too early to have been first presented at the Globe, it surely appeared in a theater with many of the same characteristics. In the play's famous "balcony scene," Juliet must have stood in such a gallery. There was possibly also a recessed, curtained area below this gallery where characters could be "revealed"—for example, the sleeping Juliet in the Capulet crypt.

Special effects were common. A trap door in the main stage allowed ghosts to appear. Even more spectacularly, supernatural beings could be lowered from above the stage. For added realism, actors hid bags of pig's blood and guts under their stage doublets. When pierced with a sword, the bags spilled out over the stage and produced a gory effect. This effect would have added excitement to the duels in *Romeo and Juliet.*

All these staging methods and design elements greatly appealed to Elizabethan audiences and made plays increasingly popular. By the time Shakespeare died in 1616, there were more than 30 theaters in and around London.

What would Shakespeare, so accustomed to the rough-and-tumble stagecraft of the Globe, think of the theaters where his plays are performed today? He would probably miss some of the vitality of the Globe. For centuries now, his plays have been most often performed on stages with a frame called the "proscenium arch," which cleanly separates the audience from the performers. This barrier tends to cast a peculiar shroud of privacy over his plays so that his characters do not seem to quite enter our world.

But with greater and greater frequency, Shakespeare's plays are being performed out-of-doors or in theaters with three- or four-sided stages. And a replica of the Globe Theatre itself opened in London in 1996, only about 200 yards from the site of the original. This new Globe may prove an exciting laboratory where directors and actors can test ideas about Elizabethan staging. Their experiments may change our ideas about how Shakespeare's plays were performed and give new insights into their meaning.

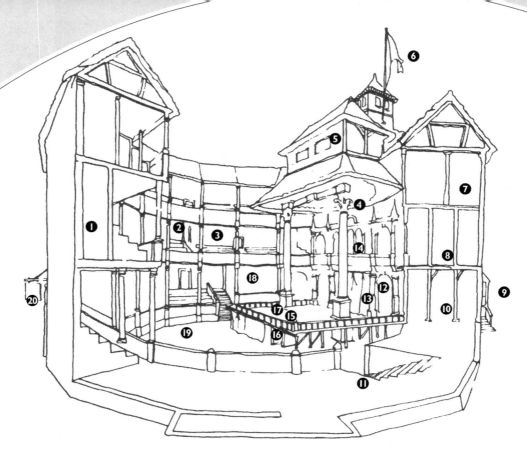

1 **Corridor** A passageway serving the middle gallery.

2 **Entrance** Point leading to the staircase and upper galleries.

3 **Middle Gallery** The seats here were higher priced.

4 **The Heavens** So identified by being painted with the zodiac signs.

5 **Hut** A storage area that also held a winch system for lowering characters to the stage.

6 **Flag** A white flag above the theater meant a show that day.

7 **Wardrobe** A storage area for costumes and props.

8 **Dressing Rooms** Rooms where actors were "attired" and awaited their cues.

9 **Tiring-House Door** The rear entrance or "stage door" for actors or privileged spectators.

10 **Tiring-House** Backstage area providing space for storage and business.

11 **Stairs** Theatergoers reached the galleries by staircases enclosed by stairwells.

12 **Stage Doors** Doors opening into the Tiring-House.

13 **Inner Stage** A recessed playing area often curtained off except as needed.

14 **Gallery** Located above the stage to house musicians or spectators.

15 **Trap Door** Leading to the Hell area where a winch elevator was located.

16 **Hell** The area under the stage, used for ghostly comings and goings or for storage.

17 **Stage** Major playing area jutting into the Pit, creating a sense of intimacy.

18 **Lords Rooms** or private galleries. Six pennies let a viewer sit here, or sometimes on stage.

19 **The Pit** Sometimes referred to as "The Yard," where the "groundlings" watched.

20 **Main Entrance** Here the doorkeeper collected admission.

The Origins and Politics of *Romeo and Juliet*

Audiences often think of *Romeo and Juliet* as a love story and nothing more. In fact, the play has a political dimension which is too frequently overlooked. The politics of *Romeo and Juliet* have their roots deep in the story's earliest Italian sources.

The play's plot goes back to several Italian novels. The first of these was written by Masuccio of Salerno during the 15th century. During the 16th century, Luigi da Porto based another novel on Masuccio's, and Bandello based yet another on Luigi's. All of these novels featured two lovers named Romeo and Giulietta whose happiness is thwarted by their feuding families, the Montecchi and Cappelletti.

During the Italian Renaissance, powerful families often quarreled violently. One feud was between the Cerchi and Donati families in Florence. They began fighting around 1300 and barely stopped for another fifty years. The Cerchi and Donati represented two opposing political factions—the Ghibellines and Guelphs, respectively. The Ghibellines (or the White faction) believed in a large Italian empire. The Guelphs (or the Black faction) favored independent city-states under the direction of the pope. Italian fans of Romeo and Giulietta may have seen the lovers as tragic pawns in the struggle over the destiny of Italy itself.

Shakespeare learned their story through Arthur Brookes' narrative poem *The Tragicall Historye of Romeus and Juliet*, published in 1562. He may have used the story of the two Italian lovers to explore a controversy in his

Florence in 1490

own time—the nature of marriage. Should marriages be arranged, or should young people choose their spouses? Is marriage simply a practical way to raise children, or should personal happiness be considered?

The controversy about marriage was influenced by religious differences. Catholics tended to see happiness in this world as less important than eternal bliss. Protestants, more concerned with worldly success, generally rated marital happiness highly—sometimes even as essential to salvation. But these divisions were by no means simple and clear-cut. The purpose of marriages and the role of parents in arranging them remained quite controversial in Shakespeare's Protestant England. Which viewpoint did Shakespeare himself hold?

Generations of English teachers have advised their students that Shakespeare and his audience were not as sympathetic to the actions of Romeo and Juliet as we are today. The play, they have said, is partly a cautionary tale about the importance of obeying one's parents. But as Cedric Watts points out, the text itself does not support this interpretation.

The love between Romeo and Juliet is necessary to bring about peace between their families. And in the speech that closes the play, Prince Escalus does not place any blame whatsoever upon the young lovers. Instead, he blames their families and even assumes some responsibility for failing to enforce the peace. If Shakespeare had felt that Romeo and Juliet were seriously at fault, surely he would have found a character to voice this viewpoint. Since he did not, we can only assume that, like Escalus, he blamed their families—and more sweepingly, a concept of marriage that did not properly value happiness. To a greater degree than is usually admitted, *Romeo and Juliet* is a play about gender politics.

Juliet and Her Romeo

Romeo's name comes first in the play's title, but Juliet is the stronger character. She, not Romeo, makes all the important decisions in the play. She is even the first to propose marriage.

Two facts about Juliet tend to surprise today's audiences and readers. One is that she is only thirteen. The other is that the part was probably first played by a teenaged boy.

On Shakespeare's stage, female roles were acted by boys. One of the most famous was John Rice, who created the roles of Lady Macbeth and Cleopatra. These parts made him something of a celebrity. Rice was even invited to make a special appearance before King James I.

The part of Juliet was probably first played by Robert Goffe. He may well have played Juliet opposite the famous tragic actor Richard Burbage. The older actor later created Hamlet, Macbeth, Othello, and King Lear. But in *Romeo and Juliet*, Goffe got the meatier role.

There is even an interesting trace of feminism in Shakespeare's play. In most romantic stories of his time, a dashing hero actively woos a beautiful but passive heroine. The hero gets to behave heroically and also to speak splendid lines as he lavishes poetry on his rather witless love object. But Juliet is *at least* Romeo's equal as an initiator of action, and her poetry often surpasses his in beauty. Consider her breathtaking pronouncement in the balcony scene: "My bounty is as boundless as the sea, / My love as deep; the more I give to thee, / The more I have, for both are infinite."

Juliet's strength and assertiveness seem all the more remarkable because her life is so limited. Like a typical well-born Renaissance girl, she can't even come and go as she pleases, much less roam the streets at night as Romeo does with his pals Mercutio and Benvolio. Again and again, we are dazzled by her determination and resourcefulness.

Juliet was first played by a woman in 1662. Samuel Pepys, who was in the audience, thought that Mrs. Saunderson gave a terrible performance. However, since that time, the role has almost always been performed by a woman. During the 19th

Charlotte Cushman

girl could legally marry at the age of twelve. For boys, the legal age was fourteen. Wealthy families sometimes arranged marriages to protect their fortunes, but early marriages were not common. The average wealthy woman in Elizabethan England married at twenty, the average wealthy man at twenty-two. Still, nobles carefully guarded the legality of early marriage and sometimes arranged for their children to marry at ages even younger than the law allowed.

Early marriage was a common enough practice to be quite controversial. Certain scholarly and medical authorities decried the practice in words similar to those of Juliet's father: "And too soon marr'd are those so early made." The danger of childbirth at such an age was widely recognized. One Elizabethan writer even insisted that women shouldn't marry before reaching the age of eighteen.

Betrothal

century, women sometimes even played the part of Romeo. The most famous female Romeo was the American actress Charlotte Cushman, who was also known for her Hamlet. (See "Tales from the Stage," p. 61)

In Shakespeare's time, women were not allowed to play dramatic roles. However, they could marry at a much earlier age than is acceptable today. In Elizabethan England, a

Romeo and Juliet Timeline

1562 Arthur Brookes publishes *The Tragicall Historye of Romeus and Juliet.*

1564 Shakespeare is baptized.

1568 Elizabeth I becomes Queen of England.

1572 Shakespeare begins grammar school.

1576 Opening of The Theatre, the first permanent playhouse in England.

1580 Drake sails around the world.

1582 Shakespeare marries Anne Hathaway.

1583 Shakespeare's daughter Susanna is baptized.

1585 Shakespeare's twins are baptized.

1588 Spanish Armada is defeated.

1592–94 Plague closes all of London's theaters.

1594 *Titus Andronicus* becomes first printed Shakespeare play.

1594 Shakespeare joins the Lord Chamberlain's Men.

1599 Lord Chamberlain's Men build the Globe Theatre; Shakespeare is part-owner of the building.

1609 *Shakespeare's Sonnets*, written in 1598, published for the first time.

The King's Men acquire the Blackfriars Playhouse.

1610 Shakespeare retires to Stratford.

1613 Globe Theatre burns to the ground.

1616 William Shakespeare dies at the age of 52.

1623 Shakespeare's wife Anne dies.

First Folio published.

Frequently Used Words

The following words and phrases are found frequently in Shakespeare's plays. The more of them you know, the easier your reading will be.

afore . . . . . before

alack . . . . . expression of sorrow or regret

alas . . . . . . expression of unhappiness, pity, or concern

anon . . . . . at once, immediately

an't . . . . . . if it

art . . . . are

ay, aye . . . . . yes

bawdy . . . . . indecent

beseech . . . . beg

betimes . . . . at times, occasionally

bid . . . . ask

by my troth . . . truly

coz . . . . cousin; relative

dost . . . . . . you do (second-person singular of the verb "do")

doth . . . . . . he, she, it does (third person singular of the verb "do")

e'en . . . . . . even

e'er . . . . . . ever

enow . . . . . enough

ere . . . . . . before

exeunt . . . . . theatre term meaning "everyone leaves the stage"

fain . . . . . . willingly

fay . . . . faith

fie . . . . O

foresworn . . . denied

hadst . . . . . . you had (second person singular past tense of the verb "have")

hap . . . . perhaps

hark you . . . . listen

hast, hath . . . . you have; he, she, it has (second and third person singular of "have")

hence . . . . . . away from this place

hie . . . . hurry

humor . . . . . mood

humour . . . . . liquid

is't . . . . is it

knave . . . . . . rascal

late	recently		**thee, thou**	you
			thence	from that time (or place) on
marry	I swear		**thine**	yours
mine	my		**thither**	there; to that place
			thrice	three times
nay	no		**thy**	your
ne'er	never		**'tis**	it is
			tut, tush	mild expression of disapproval
o'er	over		**'twixt**	between
oft	often			
			wast, wert	were
perchance	perhaps		**whence**	where (from what place)
pray	invite		**wherefore**	why
			whither	where (to what place)
rest you merry	have a good day		**wilt**	will, must
			writ	written
saucy	rude			
scurvy	disgusting		**ye**	you
shalt	you shall (second-person singular of "shall")		**yea**	yes
shrift	confession of sins		**yon, yond**	that
sirrah	sir (a form of address implying inferiority)			
soft	wait			
spake	said			
stay	stop			
straight	at once			
sup	to eat (often the evening meal)